Leaving the Bedside

The Search for a Nonclinical Medical Career

Revised Edition

Acknowledgments

The following made significant contributions to the revision of this book. Their efforts are both acknowledged and appreciated.

Senior Editor
Mark Ingebretsen
Trade Publishing
American Medical Association

Product Line Development Director
Suzanne Fraker
Product Line Development
American Medical Association

The first edition of this book was researched by Joe Ann Jackson, then Director of the AMA Physicians Career Resource, and written by Maija Balagot, a Chicago-based communications consultant.

The American Medical Association gratefully acknowledges the valuable assistance provided by the following people:

Jonathan Burkhardt, AMA; Wesley Curry, American College of Physician Executives; Michael Doody, Kieffer, Ford and Hadelman; Pat Dragisic, AMA; Steven Ellwing, AMA; Gerald Farley, AMA; Joyce Flory, Communications for Business; Harvey R. Forester, MD; Jay A. Gold, MD, JD, American College of Legal Medicine; Lee S. Goldsmith, MD, LLB, Goldsmith & Tabak, PC; Randy Gott, Jackson and Coker; Richard Harris, MD; Bruce Herman, Bruce Rogers Company; Herb Hinkelman, AMA; Arlene Hirsch, MA, Arlene Hirsch and Associates; Gigi Hirsch, MD, Center for Physician Development; Marilyn Huebel; Martin D. Keller, MD; Daniel L. Kisner, MD; Phyllis R. Kopriva, AMA; Janet Laybold, DePaul University College of Law; Anne White Michalski, AMA; David Orentlicher, MD, JD, AMA; Celia Paul, Celia Paul Associates; Sharon Pierce, Pierce and Associates; Paul J. Pierron, DO; Marshall Rosman, AMA; T. Donald Rucker, PhD; Mark Saberman, MD, John Muir Medical Foundation; Mary Sexton, MEd, and Elliot M. Sogol, PhD, Glaxo Wellcome Pathway Evaluation Program; Andrew Stewart, AMA; Phil Szenas, Association of American Medical Colleges; Chuck Woeppel, Jackson and Coker; and Allan P. Wolff, MD.

Contents

**Part 1:
Considering a
Change**

Introduction

As a practicing physician, are you considering leaving patient care—or leaving medicine altogether? Or, as a resident, are you having second thoughts about your plans to practice medicine?

Take comfort in the fact that you're not alone. One search firm that specializes in placing physicians in the pharmaceutical and biotechnology industries receives almost 300 inquiries a month from doctors who are eager to leave patient care.[1] Competent, caring doctors are discovering that, for a variety of reasons, they're not happy practicing medicine, and they're exploring other options—in or out of medicine.

Until recently, "the idea of physicians leaving the practice of medicine was anathema.... It simply wasn't done by *successful* physicians," wrote career consultant Marilyn Moats Kennedy in *Group Practice Journal*.[2] "It's being done now. The number of physicians making successful changes, particularly from direct delivery of medical care to administration or management, is increasing. To alter career focus, physicians are going through the same learning and decision-making process as professionals in other fields—they're considering their 'options.'"

According to the US Department of Labor, anywhere from 9% to 12% of all working people switch occupations each year.[3] Anyone in the process of even considering a career change knows the roller-coaster feelings that change can engender: anxiety, depression, denial, self-doubt, anger, and fear—along with hope, acceptance, and exhilaration. Physicians considering a career change face particular stresses and can feel especially isolated because of the time and resources they put into becoming a physician, their high expectations of themselves, and the role they play in society as doctors.

Which is why we're here.

We don't presume to know, of course, what's best for you or for anyone: whether it's continuing in practice, finding something nonclinical within the field of medicine, or exploring something outside of medicine altogether. What we shall try to offer is a guide to the career-change process, an exploration of some career options, and some suggestions about job-search strategies—all toward the goal of helping physicians find satisfying, successful work.

To make informed career decisions, people need information about themselves (first) and information about their options (second). Only then should they take action. The order is important. The process a career counselor guides a client through typically involves three stages: assessing values and skills, exploring career options, and then formulating an action plan. The three sections of this publication roughly parallel those stages.

Part 1, "Considering a Change," explores the psychology of career change and addresses the issues specific to physicians, including the reasons why physicians are considering leaving patient care—or leaving medicine altogether. Although this section can't claim to be a substitute for one-on-one career counseling, it at least raises some of the issues. It invites reflection on questions such as: What do I enjoy doing? What's important to me? What do I want to get out of life? And what are my skills?

Part 2, "Nonclinical Career Opportunities for Physicians," addresses the question: What fields are open to my skills? It explores several fields in which physicians have found employment. We've limited our exploration mostly to careers that are still related to medicine—not so much because of any prejudice on our part but because that's our area of expertise. Many MDs have indeed found happiness entirely outside of medicine—as novelists, real estate developers, or presidents of stock firms. However, as we'll discuss in part 1, the transition out of medicine and into another work culture raises additional issues for the career changer.

The careers covered in part 2 are only a sampling of what's available, not an exhaustive survey. Physicians who have found satisfying "alternative" careers often created their own opportunities or, at the very least, were poised psychologically to recognize and take advantage of an opportunity when it came along. Although we cover the pharmaceutical industry and the work of physician executives (in a variety of settings)—which are the two places where the greatest number of non-patient-care jobs seem to be (or the places, at least, that receive the most press)—our philosophy has been: if there's only one doctor doing it or 1000 doctors doing it, it still may be worth our exploring on your behalf.

Part 3, "Taking the Next Step," addresses the question: How do I go about finding the job I want? For many physicians (as many as 90%, in one career counselor's estimation), the job they want is the one they already have. After reflecting on their values, assessing their skills, and exploring other options, they conclude, "Maybe I'm happier practicing medicine than I thought I was," and they decide to continue practicing medicine—but with a fresh outlook and perhaps a new angle.

Once you have a sense of which path you'll follow, this section will help you create an action plan and set goals. It provides tips on writing an effective curriculum vitae and offers advice from search consultants on how to work effectively with search firms.

The American Medical Association welcomes your comments—especially your suggestions on how to enhance this publication's usefulness, as well as your ideas about what fields should be explored for possible future editions. In the meantime, we wish you happiness—along with success in your journey toward a satisfying career.

Notes

1. Crane M. Thinking about leaving practice? Read this first. *Medical Economics.* August 15, 1988:132-136.

2. Kennedy MM. Making a move and keeping your family, too. *Group Practice Journal.* September/October 1985:72-76. Ms Kennedy is the founder and managing partner of Career Strategies, a consulting firm in Winnetka, Ill. Quoted with permission of the American Group Practice Association.

3. Moskowitz R. Why retire? You can have a second career. *Investor's Business Daily.* April 21, 1995:A1

Part 1
Considering a Change

**Feeling Pushed—
or Pulled?**

Physicians consider leaving patient care for almost as many reasons as there are physicians:

- A cardiologist who has suffered a partial hearing loss wonders how long he'll be able to continue practicing.

- An exhausted pediatrician in Illinois wants more-predictable hours, less time on call, and more time with her children.

- A physician in New Hampshire yearns for that elusive "something more." He's discovered he enjoys teaching, but prefers education outside of medicine—perhaps he'll teach biology, he says.

- A New York City internist has developed an interest in public policy and journalism; she thinks she wants to write about medical topics for the layperson.

- After just 1 year in practice, a pediatrician working in a low-income clinic feels burned out on the bureaucracy and on the callousness of some coworkers.[1]

- An otolaryngologist feels fed up with "kooky" patients who come to him with hidden agendas, who lie about their medical histories, who seemingly just want to use him as a pawn in their malpractice suits—and who don't pay their bills.

- A psychiatrist is exhausted from dealing with hospital politics, cost-containment edicts, and battles over turf. "My work is challenging," she says, "but I feel agitated most of the time."[2]

- A 35-year-old primary care physician employed by an HMO is placed on probation because of her disruptive outbursts of temper at work. Through counseling, she realizes what is causing her frustration: her lack of control over her schedule (and the secretary who manages it), combined with increasing demands from the HMO for productivity. She tries to solve the problem through the proper organizational channels but is unsuccessful.[3]

- In response to an increase in state regulations that impose on the practice patterns of physicians, a California surgeon concludes that "physicians need to be represented in forums where decisions about the care of individuals in our society [are] made." He studies first for a JD and then for an MBA, eventually practicing surgery part-time while serving as an assistant medical director.[4]

- A new internist in Connecticut, finally settling into solo practice—the career he had selected for himself more than a decade earlier—feels dissatisfied. "I cannot say that it [isn't] what I expected, only that it [isn't] enough. I...feel isolated on the edges of medicine."[5] He leaps at an opportunity to get into management, eventually becoming a vice president for health sciences at a university health center.

- A Massachusetts physician who still believes in making house calls often gets yelled at by patients. Feeling unappreciated and fed up, she accepts a job as the head of a university health service.[6]

- A surgeon whose father had also been a physician complains that competition is "cutthroat," the reimbursement rules set up by the Blues and Medicare are "restrictive"—even "hostile"—and his practice is nothing like the one his father enjoyed. He plans to concentrate on purchasing real estate and studying for a broker's license—spending more time with pursuits more profitable than medicine. After only a few years, medicine has become a burden for him; he wants to retire as soon as possible.[7]

The reasons why doctors consider leaving medicine can be divided into two types: "push" factors and "pull" factors; doctors feel pushed out of medicine and/or pulled toward something else. The push factors include the following:

- Disillusionment with medicine

- The impact of managed care

- The physician's own medical problems

- Financial considerations

- Threat of increased litigation

- Environmental factors

The pull factors include changing needs, values, and interests, and the desire to make a contribution elsewhere.

Those in the latter group—feeling pulled toward something else—are perhaps the luckier: the physician who feels strongly drawn by the challenges of, say, a leadership position as a physician executive probably feels less stressed and more in control during the transition than the physician who feels forced out of practice by a decline in fee-for-service patients (and is now scrambling to meet his or her office-staff payroll).

Disillusionment

That doctors are dissatisfied with practicing medicine is not a new story: accounts abound in the medical press. For some, the dissatisfaction is a matter of unmet expectations. The realities of practicing medicine today differ greatly from physicians' fantasies of how it would be. The difference can be jarring; some feel deceived when the day-to-day reality of the actual work is so far off from their expectations. Says one doctor, "If someone had told me that this is what it would be like, I never would have done it."[8]

Some doctors are frustrated with the patients themselves. "I *love* sick people," says an otolaryngologist who remains in practice despite his dissatisfaction. "A patient comes in, I treat them, and they get better—that gives me a lot of satisfaction. But it's not like that with many of the people I see." He offered this graphic example: "I was called to the hospital stat to deal with a man who'd beaten his wife many times. This one night, she responded by slitting his throat from ear to ear with a serrated bread knife. When I got to the hospital I didn't stop to fill out forms—we just jumped in and did what needed to be done. It was a very close call, and we spent a lot of time stitching him up. Believe it or not, he walked out of the hospital a week later. He came to see me for follow-up—of course he didn't have a dime—and you know what he says? He points to his neck, which was healing up nicely. 'Doctor,' he says, 'I don't like the scar you gave me.'

"I'd never recommend this to my kids," the physician continued. "I tell them to become plumbers. They'll have fewer headaches—and they actually may get paid."

For other physicians, it's not so much that they're angered and frustrated by patients—they've simply discovered that patient care isn't their cup of tea. Celia Paul is a New York City–based career consultant who has advised hundreds of physicians. She recently counseled one MD who decided to go into research, because the MD was someone who really didn't enjoy working with patients. "That actually sounds like a joke," Paul said, "but we hear a lot of that—people who became doctors but they don't really enjoy working with patients. That client was more interested in the scientific part of medicine." Another of Paul's clients made the same self-discovery while doing a residency to be an internist. "Internal medicine is a ridiculous field for someone like that," said Paul, "because there's so much patient care." The internist went into nuclear medicine.

Sometimes the physician's dissatisfaction is due to a mismatch between the patients as a group and the physician. What the otolaryngologist above (who practices in an economically declining neighborhood) would perhaps find as a relief—treating middle-class patients who have routine problems and who pay their bills—another physician (one interested in, say, doing health-care outreach to immigrant populations) might find unchallenging and unsatisfying. It's valid to structure your practice around not just the medical services you want to offer but also the population you want to serve. A mismatch can add stress to an already stressful situation.

Fantasy vs reality

Arlene Hirsch, a psychotherapist and career consultant in Chicago, has counseled many professionals. Before today's doctors became doctors, she told us, they probably had fantasies about what life as a doctor was going to be like. For many, those fantasies have not been fulfilled, and that's where the feeling of disappointment comes in, along with the desire to get out. For example, "they may have expected people to idealize them," she said. "And some people really don't idealize doctors any more. And they may have expected the work to be different, less hands-on. Some people who consider medicine as a career don't really think about the *work* of being a doctor; instead, they picture the status and they picture the money. But much of the work itself is not glamorous—in fact, it may not even be enjoyable. Sometimes they have a fantasy about helping people, and that being a doctor is going to be more rewarding than it sometimes is. They think they're going to save people, and you can't always save lives. You lose some, and that is disillusioning. And there's also the fantasy that people will be grateful; but they're not always grateful."

In fact, as some physicians have discovered, instead of being grateful, patients criticize you—or sue you at the drop of a hat.

"For a lot of people," continued Hirsch, "this idea of being a doctor starts very young. It has to do with the need to do something important, to be admired, and to achieve. Being a doctor is the quintessential achievement. And if other people don't view it that way, that's disillusioning."

As people grow, their needs change, and it becomes time to move on to other issues. For example, a young person's need to be admired turns into an adult's need to enjoy what he or she is doing on a day-to-day basis.

"The people who are happiest with their careers and who don't change careers," said Hirsch, "are the ones who enjoy the process and the discovery and the challenge and the excitement of the day-to-day activities. It's the intrinsic daily rewards that keep people satisfied. In general, this is something people don't realize when they're choosing careers."

The paycheck at the end of the month is *part* of it; if you're not compensated appropriately, then you're still going to be discouraged, Hirsch explained. "But people who are focusing too much on the extrinsic rewards will ultimately get the sense that they're giving up too much of their time for something they're not enjoying. They wind up cramming their life into the weekend. And those people really struggle."

If you find pleasure in the day-to-day, Hirsch concluded, then you'll like your career. "And I believe you'll find ways to make a living at it," she added.

The impact of managed care

Many physicians continue to love the actual work of practicing medicine and treating patients, but they feel pushed away from medicine by external factors. The physician-patient interaction was once straightforward: the doctor treated the patient, and the patient paid for the service. Now intruding into that relationship is the complex of insurance companies, medical management organizations, and restrictive systems and procedures called managed care. Managed-care networks control access to and payment for health care services, using such systems and techniques as case-by-case utilization review, contracts with selected health care professionals, financial incentives or disincentives, and compensation based on capitation (fixed fee per patient).[9] These methods tend to undermine some of the traditional privileges that physicians once enjoyed. Managed care has become one of the chief sources of physician dissatisfaction.

Although managed care is not the only reason physicians are leaving their practices, it is a significant one. In a 1995 survey of office-based MDs and DOs conducted by *Medical Economics*, 21% of doctors over 50 years old said they wanted to retire or sell their practices within a year.[10] A San Francisco survey of 173 practitioners in the area of mental health (which has been profoundly affected by managed care) found that 43% were considering leaving the field.[11]

Most physicians have little choice in becoming involved with managed-care systems. Because of rising medical costs, employers are switching their insurance benefits from traditional indemnity or fee-for-service plans to managed-care plans. Enrollment in US HMOs was projected to reach nearly 65 million people in 1996, an increase of more than 25% from 1995.[12] Seven of 10 patients are now enrolled in managed-care plans.[13] That figure is even steeper in areas where managed care has been in place longer, such as Sacramento, California, where 96% of the population is now in managed-care programs.[14]

Many people are attracted to the medical professions in part because of the authority, autonomy, and independence they offer. Under managed-care systems, physicians have less authority, less autonomy, less independence; they are accountable not just to themselves and their peers, but to nonphysician managers who may question their medical judgment on economic grounds. Physicians making the switch to managed-care systems often feel this loss of control deeply.

Gigi Hirsch, MD, director of the Center for Physician Development, sees this frequently as she counsels physicians contemplating a career change. "A lot of individuals are feeling quite powerless right now, and the fact of the matter is that they *are*," said Hirsch in a recent telephone interview. "The managed-care environment is really making people stop and reflect about their values, their motivations for becoming a doctor, whether they're going to be able to achieve their fundamental mission in the current environment, and whether their goals and the possibility of reaching them are so incongruent at this point that a change becomes essential."

Physicians are trained to make quick and accurate diagnoses and to treat the patient with a minimum of delay, especially in emergency situations. The medical education system teaches physicians that they have the answers, and that they are in charge. Under managed-care systems, physicians are not in charge. The treatments they prescribe are reviewed and sometimes questioned or rejected by nonphysician utilization-review managers. Treatments may be delayed longer than the physician would like because of administrative procedure. Emergency room physicians are sometimes forced to send noncritical patients away because the patient's HMO policy requires preapproval. Even if the physician is not directly employed by the managed-care network, the relationship between the network and the physician is often like that of employer-employee —a very different situation from the professional autonomy the physician functioned under previously.

In some managed-care systems, physicians have financial incentives to limit treatment or disincentives to prescribe treatment, or they are forbidden by the terms of their contract to inform the patient of treatments that may possibly be effective but that are not covered under the terms of the program. These factors not only place the physician in a tricky ethical situation, but they also diminish the role of the physician as the patient's advocate. People become physicians because they want to help people, and managed-care policies and procedures may seem to them to be a hindrance.

Managed care involves increasing amounts of administrative work. Written approval from an insurance company is often required before treatment can be given. Between 1968 and 1993, the number of health care workers in the US doing administrative work grew by 692%; the number of physicians grew by only 77%.[15] Physicians in solo practices often must handle this paperwork themselves. One California physician in solo practice spends 5 hours every week tending to paperwork.[16]

Managed health care is evolving quickly, and both patient and physician dissatisfaction may influence and change managed-care policies and procedures in the future. But it is unlikely that medical practice will ever be the same. Managed care has changed both the rules and the playing field, and these new conditions will continue to cause physicians to question their careers.

Resources for additional information on managed care

National Association of Managed Care Physicians
4435 Waterfront Dr
PO Box 4765
Glen Allen, VA 23058-4765
800 722-0376

Publishes *Managed Care Medicine* (bimonthly magazine) and *NAMCP Guide to Managed Care Medicine* (monograph).

The American Medical Association offers several publications designed to help keep physicians up to date with the latest developments in managed health care, including *Managing Managed Care in the Medical Practice; Capitation: The Physician's Guide; Managed Care Strategies for Physicians; Implementing a Physician Organization;* and *Medical Practices and Managed Care* (newsletter). To order, call 800 621-8335.

Physician's medical problems

The physician's own medical problems—stress, disability, sensory impairment, hampered mobility, drug or alcohol addiction, and so on—can be a push factor, forcing him or her to consider leaving practice. Disability insurance claims with one major insurer of physicians jumped 60% in the first 6 months of 1994. Most of the claims involved a degree of impairment that the physicians were able to ignore as long as they felt motivated and rewarded by their jobs, an official of the insurer said.[17]

Although disability sometimes leads physicians to leave practice, it would be a mistake to assume that one automatically follows the other. In some cases, the issue may be one of learning to come to terms with the medical condition and making necessary adjustments in the physician's practice. One of Celia Paul's clients, a 50-year-old internist interviewed in *Medical Economics*,[18] thought at first that he was going through a midlife crisis, and then admitted his real concern: a partial hearing loss was making it hard to practice. After exploring his values and options, he decided to work more on dealing with his disability.

In cases where stress is causing or contributing to physical ailments, drug or alcohol addiction, or feelings of burnout, the answer may be to come to terms with the conditions causing that stress. If your stress is caused by career dissatisfaction, you can use some of the tools in this book to reassess your abilities, talents, and goals and find a new direction. Stress caused by the increasing pressures brought on physicians by managed care is harder to deal with, because the stress-causing factors are not entirely in your control.

Some of these factors can be dealt with by adopting new techniques and strategies in your practice (see "Finding New Life in an Old Career," page 33). If your stress is caused by the working conditions of your managed-care arrangement, you can research different managed-care options and seek out those arrangements that will work best for you.

Nearly every state has a physician health program (sometimes known as the impaired physician program, physician recovery program, etc) through its state medical society. Many of these programs handle a range of issues from malpractice stress to burnout to HIV infection and physical disability.

Additional resources include the following:

American Association for the Advancement of Science
1200 New York Ave NW
Washington, DC 20005
202 326-6672
Sponsors: Project on Science, Technology, and Disability

Association of Academic Physiatrists
7100 Lakewood Bldg
5987 E 71st St, Suite 112
Indianapolis, IN 46220
317 845-4200
Provides: Networking opportunities; publications

The Center for Physician Development
1 Memorial Dr, 15th Floor
Cambridge, MA 02142
617 252-0241
Provides: Career counseling; professional development, stress management.

Aging/retirement

The awareness that one is aging, coupled with a feeling of disenchantment with medicine, can be a double whammy for the older physician. A recent survey shows that physicians, out of dissatisfaction with the profession, are retiring or selling their practices earlier and in increasing numbers[19]; physician attrition has accelerated in older age groups.[20] Some middle-aged physicians are taking a hard look at their options because they feel that they may not have another chance to make a change in their lives, and they want to see what other kinds of work are available.

Some physicians are blessed with the foresight to plan ahead. Anticipating the time when they'll no longer have the desire or the ability to see patients, they're asking themselves, "What else could I do?" Paul Pierron, DO, a family practitioner in his late 30s, has taken on a part-time consulting job in part because he's thinking ahead to retirement. As a consultant to a managed-care organization, his job is to get patients into appropriate settings and get them what they need as inexpensively and quickly as possible. The part-time nonclinical work, which amounts to about 10% of his workload, helps him stay current in his field while preparing him for nonclinical work in later years.

Financial considerations

No one needs to tell an audience of physicians that medical education is extremely expensive. According to the Association of American Medical Colleges, 81.5% of senior medical students in 1995 had student-loan debt, and the average level of indebtedness for seniors with debt was $69,059. Of the indebted 1995 senior medical students, 21.6% had debt in levels between $50,000 and $74,999, while 33.2% graduated with debt in excess of $75,000.

This, coupled with the long hours and low pay of residency, enormously high practice start-up costs, and mean professional expenses of self-employed physicians of $182,200 (1993),[21] can make new physicians poor, tired, and angry. They expected to make personal sacrifices to be in medicine, and they're prepared for the long hours and hard work. But they may not be prepared for the debt.

Furthermore, they may not be prepared for the effect of the debt, which is to channel doctors into highly paid urban specialties and away from rural settings and specialties like obstetrics and gynecology. If the urban specialty is what the physician wanted, fine; but for many, that wasn't their plan. From the patients' point of view, the debt has a negative effect, too: for example, there are whole areas of the country where there are no OB/GYN practitioners.

Some established physicians reconsider their careers because their income needs rise: their children are entering college or they have the costs of caring for an aging parent. Conversely, some consider leaving medicine because they finally can afford to: their children have all been put through college, their mortgage is paid off, and they're no longer burdened by medical school or practice start-up debts. They're finally able to address quality-of-life questions that may have been put off for decades.

One of the chief rewards for the personal sacrifices required of physicians has been the high levels of financial compensation that a medical career brings. But even this traditional benefit is being eroded. In 1993, median physician net income fell 3.8%, the first-ever drop in income recorded by the AMA. The AMA attributed the drop to three factors: increasing overhead costs, stabilizing Medicare compensation, and cost pressures from managed care. Although physician income had increased each year between 1984 to 1994 by an average of 5% (greater than the inflation rate of 3.6%), such increases in income were not expected in the near future.[22]

Specialists in areas where managed care has achieved greater market penetration report even greater losses in income. In San Diego, where competitive pressures are unusually high, many specialists have seen their incomes cut by as much as 30% to 40%, according to the chair of the economic issues committee of the San Diego County Medical Society.[23]

Increased threat of litigation

High malpractice-insurance premiums, along with the constant feeling that you have to "cover yourself" against lawsuits, can have a debilitating effect on physicians' morale.

Patients these days are quicker to cry foul—they're more vocal with their disappointments. We're not here to discount their complaints; however, the phenomenon, as it applies to physicians' morale, is of interest. Arlene Hirsch explains it this way: "That's the negative transference, I think. In many cases, because something goes wrong, the assumption [on the part of the patient] is that somebody *did* something wrong. Therefore, you [as the patient] have to find someone to blame, and you should then be entitled to receive something for your pain. And since doctors make all this money, and you went to them and they were supposed to fix you, they're the ones who should be paying you back for your loss. And they *must* have done something wrong—it *couldn't* be that you were unfixable." Or that sometimes things happen—and it is nobody's fault.

Sometimes the motive for a lawsuit is based on the patient's unmet, perhaps unrealistic, expectations. The patient's real argument is, "You disappointed me! You didn't save me! You let down my expectations!" And for some physicians, that in itself is stress enough to push them out of the field.

Physicians working under managed-care contracts often face increased liability risk. Managed-care plans generally increase the responsibility and obligations of primary-care "gatekeeper" physicians while limiting their choice of services and specialists. The financial incentives offered to physicians through managed-care plans may leave the physician open to a claim that he or she failed to provide proper care due to financial self-interest.[24]

Physician competition and oversupply

Most managed-care experts agree that as cost-containment measures increase, the need for hospital beds and physicians, especially specialists, will decline, making the market even more competitive.[25] A 1996 report from the Institute of Medicine called for reducing the supply of physicians in several ways, including freezing the number of medical schools and their class sizes and limiting the medical school slots available to foreign physicians.[26] Until recently, those who chose a medical career were virtually guaranteed a job for life. Physicians feeling competitive pressures may seek to choose another specialty (see page 36) or look for an alternative career.

"Wrong" choice

Celia Paul, a New York City career consultant, says her physician clients can be loosely divided into two groups: (1) those who are still interested in practicing medicine but are having difficulties with the business side of practice (read the section "Finding New Life in an Old Career," page 33) and (2) those who made the wrong original choice.

Some physicians, feeling frustrated and disillusioned in middle life, conclude that medicine may have been the "wrong" choice, when perhaps it really wasn't: it was simply the best choice they could make based on the information at hand and their needs at the time.

Many of us made career choices based on inadequate information. (It can be argued that to a certain extent the life choices we make are always based on inadequate information, because none of us can predict our futures.)

Some of us made our career choices very early in life—even as young as 13. Those choices may have reflected the legitimate needs of the person we were at 13: for example, the need for recognition from our teachers, approval from our parents, and status among our peers. The problems arise when we're still living out those choices at age 30 or 40 or 50 and they don't fit our adult selves. Our need for recognition may give way to a need for self-expression; our need for high status may give way to a need to be a responsible, capable parent; or our desire to please our parents may give way to a need to please ourselves. We outgrow our adult choices, too: the ones we make at 40 sometimes don't fit us at 50, and so on. Throughout our lives we need to be willing to evaluate how well our work fits our values, interests, and needs.

Our choices are based on our fantasies and expectations about the future; we imagine when we're 17 or 18 that when we're an adult we'll want to be rich, important, and admired—which, in our society, is equated with being a doctor. We have no way of anticipating that at age 40 our strongest interests will be international politics, spending quiet time with our families, or building model ships—and not spending evenings and weekends working in the ER.

Today's physicians, when they were medical students, may not have received the information they needed for making a good choice about a specialty. According to a 1987 nationwide survey of medical students by Glaxo Inc,[27] most medical students (80% of the 314 respondents) did not feel very well informed about what it would be like to practice in the specialties they were considering.

The students expressed a clear need for additional information on which to base their decisions, while agreeing that choice of specialty was the most important decision they faced in medical school.

The question we would pose is this: should those medical students beat themselves up 5 or 10 years down the road when they discover, as physicians, that they're not suited to their specialty?

Gigi Hirsch, MD, director of the Center for Physician Development in Boston, believes that the pressures of managed care often make physicians question their career decisions. "Most physicians who come here tell us that they've known for some time that they're in the wrong specialty, or perhaps in the wrong profession, and that they made the wrong choice early on," Hirsch said in a phone interview. "But because of many of the extrinsic rewards of being a physician in the old model, they were able to make their peace with it. They were able to feel that they were doing good things for people, having a positive impact on the world. They also had a certain level of status, and they were reimbursed adequately. What's happened in the restructuring of the health care industry is that a lot of those extrinsic rewards have been undermined and eroded. At a certain point, that tips the scale for them, and they make the decision that they really don't want to continue doing what they're doing anymore."

Physician dissatisfaction

While the number of physicians involved in non-patient care dropped by less than 2,000 between 1980 and 1994, the actual ratio of physicians involved in non-patient care has dropped from 15.8% in 1980 to 10% in 1994, according to the AMA Division of Survey and Data Resources (see table, next page).

What has changed, of course, is the number of MDs in the country. In 1980, there were 373,503 MDs in the United States. By 1994, the total number of MDs had risen to 529,476. United States physicians involved in patient care have watched their ranks swell from 314,470 (in 1980) to 472,181 (in 1994).

Regular Practicing Physicians in the United States, 1980–1994

(Does not include students or residents, or physicians listed as inactive or "address unknown.")

	1980	1990	1994
Total number of MDs	373,503	476,599	529,476
Number of MDs involved in patient care	314,470	420,481	472,181
Number of MDs involved in non-patient care	59,033	56,118	57,295
Percentage of total MDs involved in non-patient care	15.8%	11.8%	10.0%

Source: *Physician Characteristics and Distribution, 1995–96 Edition.* Department of Data Survey and Planning, Division of Survey and Data Resources, American Medical Association, 1995.

The Courage to Change

Physicians who are unhappy practicing medicine may feel embarrassed to admit that after all the time, effort, and money involved in getting their education, they just don't get the same charge out of patient care as their colleagues do. When so many people envy a physician's career, physicians can feel shame and guilt when they admit to themselves they're not satisfied. Oftentimes, relatives and friends don't seem to understand the physician's pain, and the physician concludes that he or she is a failure. Doctors who want out of pressures like long hours, threats of litigation, and life-and-death situations are neither losers nor incompetents.

The average person spends at least a third of his or her life at work; the average doctor spends more. If the activities that take up so much of our lives don't give us satisfaction—or worse, they bring unhappiness—then it makes sense to remedy the situation. Indeed, we owe it to ourselves.

Arlene Hirsch, a psychotherapist and career consultant in Chicago, advised, "Think about how much of your life is tied up in being a doctor. If you don't enjoy the day-to-day process of practicing medicine, then that means you're sacrificing at least a third of your life to something that isn't giving you any intrinsic satisfaction." If physicians don't enjoy their work, they may look for more rewards from the environment, relying to an even greater extent on the money and power and status of being a doctor to keep them feeling good about themselves—a cycle that can lead to more dissatisfaction in the long term. Therefore, although the process of taking an honest look at one's level of career satisfaction may seem risky, it affords a wonderful opportunity: the chance to reclaim a third of our lives.

For physicians, considering a change has its particular difficulties. Although as a group they possess higher than average intelligence, a record of high achievement, and sophisticated skills (and thus have access to more opportunities than laypeople), the pressure not to change—to stay in medicine at all costs—can be enormous. A doctor who says he or she doesn't want to be a doctor anymore is seen as a hedonist—or a lunatic. *But you've got it so good!* the lay public thinks. *How could you give up* that—*this thing I couldn't possibly achieve, even if I wanted to?*

Hirsch frequently runs support groups for career changers in Chicago. The participants come from diverse fields and diverse levels, but they have one thing in common: they're all surprised to learn that other people are unhappy. Disbelief was one group's first reaction to an opera singer who told the group she didn't want to be an opera singer anymore. But after hearing about the pressures she faced—how few jobs there are and the intense competition—they got it; they understood.

In this society doctors are put in the role of superparent, expected to take care of patients—forever and ever. Doctors themselves, trained on a diet of duty, obligation, high achievement, and dedication, can feel enormous conflict when they realize that the career in which they've invested 20 or more years isn't bringing them happiness.

The psychological challenge to a physician changing careers is real: it requires a willingness to let go of your whole notion of what you are—and to let go of how you want the world to see you. Until you're ready to release your ideas of who and what you are, you may not be able to see the new possibilities.

"To me, when doctors want to leave medicine," says Hirsch, "it's one of the more painful kinds of changes, just because of the investment involved. Some doctors chose medicine from day one, or they had very early ideas about practicing medicine. So they come in without a clue, and their identity is tied up in being a doctor. [A career counselor] needs to help them address what it would feel like to give up the status, and sometimes the income, and develop a whole new self image around a different vocation. Where we have to start is with the issue of identity, and that makes it more complicated."

How can you make it easier on yourself? A career change can be an emotional roller coaster; be sure to ask for the support you need. Take time to reflect and to get in touch with activities you've enjoyed in the past. Walk on the beach, go away for the weekend, and turn off the phones, the beeper, and the fax machine. Talk with people you love and trust. And talk with others in your situation. Whatever your situation is, there *are* people who share it, even if only certain aspects of it. Talk to them! Compare notes with other doctors who are considering leaving medicine. Spend time with people who are interested in the field you're thinking about moving into. Talk to other people who share your financial pressures: people who are either looking for ways to boost their incomes or who are trying to downsize to a more modest lifestyle. Most of all, track down and talk to other career changers; it'll be a relief to discover you're not the only unhappy soul on the face of the earth.

Deborah L. Arron's book, *Running From the Law: Why Good Lawyers Are Getting Out of the Legal Profession,*[28] offers advice that also pertains to physician career changers: Let go of the notion that you owe a lifetime commitment to your current employer or partners, or even to your professional career. Just because you've done something—and done it well—for 20 years doesn't mean you have to do it for another 20. Many professionals these days look at their careers in terms of decade-long, not lifelong, commitments: they expect to give a particular career their all for 10 years or so and then move on to something else.

Don't jump into another field without thorough reflection, research, and planning. Although a willingness to take action and take risks is important, there are no quick fixes when it comes to life planning; you need to think through all the repercussions and be prepared for them as best you can. But don't put off your career decision until you lose your job or get burned out! And beware of getting additional training unless it's really necessary for your new career or you have a burning desire to learn more about the field; going back to school can simply be a way of delaying the issues and decisions that you need to face today.

Also, don't jump into another field just because you've read about it in a book or magazine article or you've heard many of your peer physicians are doing it. Gigi Hirsch, MD, director of the Center for Physician Development, cautions against jumping onto the management or law-degree bandwagon just because there are organizations and programs designed to help you do that. "We see some physicians who are in a hurry to make a change," says Hirsch. "They grab for some clearly defined path, for example, going into management. That's the path of least resistance, to simply comply with paths that are already carved out."

But those paths, just because they're laid out and easy to follow, are not necessarily the right paths for you to follow. Explains Hirsch, "Some people who made a mistake by going into medicine make the exact same mistake, in terms of the process they use, by grabbing onto a law degree or an MBA—simply because it's there and because they need to define themselves. And they don't stop and think this time around about what it is they really want, what it is they're going to be able to do with that degree, how it will affect their life and their lifestyle, and whether that degree is going to really give them what they're looking for."

Changing Peer Groups

A physician considering a major change, such as moving from practicing to *not* practicing, may feel, for a time, like a person without a country. He or she will be out of sync with the old peer group (practicing physicians) and not yet connected to the new one (if he or she even knows what it'll be). Typically, people in this situation feel as though they're the only person on the face of the earth who's ever been there—and that illusion just adds to the stress they're experiencing.

Mark Saberman, MD, a California physician administrator, can attest to that. After a rewarding 25-year career, Saberman saw the managed care revolution coming over a period of many years and decided to make the switch to an administrative role. He became medical director of a large managed-care organization, and readily admits that it was difficult to leave his peer group of physicians. Saberman says, "It's very sobering, having most of your professional life been one of the physician community, collegially accepted, and now being suddenly separated from that. You begin to feel isolated." Now Saberman feels that his colleagues are other physician administrators. "They're the people who understand me and how I feel best."

It's hard to be without a peer group, feeling cast adrift from our usual role in life. To sustain motivation, what one needs most is the knowledge that others are going and have gone through a similar process—and have survived. It's important to connect with other career changers, other people who have the courage to go against the grain. They will function as an *interim peer group,* giving you colleagues to identify with while you're searching.

Arlene Hirsch advises that physicians not jump to a new peer group (composed of, say, medical managers) too quickly, "because I think you need to go through that transitional phase where you mourn the old. And if you attach too quickly to something new, as a way of defending against that anxiety, then it would be incomplete. You won't get the full benefit of what you're trying to achieve.

"Find individuals whose value systems allow them to support individual change that requires some courage, even a change that involves giving up a high-status profession," Hirsch continued. "Find people who will admire it. Some people will genuinely love you and try to understand, but you have to recognize that others have their own agendas. Your career change may be hard on them, and they are probably not the right people to be talking to about it."

Where do you find people who will understand? In career-change workshops or support groups, through networking, and in your family.

Adjusting to a New Playing Field

One of the problems doctors run into when they change careers, Hirsch said, is that people have a certain image of what doctors do, along with an idea of what their personalities are about. "People are going to have trouble fitting that image with what the doctor is doing now. Doctors are fine in health care, but if you're not in a health-care organization, people will have a hard time trusting that you can really understand their culture and be a part of it." Even if you've taken off your doctor's hat, everyone else will keep putting it back on.

"Whatever stereotype people have about doctors is what they're going to apply to you," Hirsch added. "You've got to sell yourself in that new environment—and it may be a hard sell. As long as you as a physician are still within health care, you're on safer ground because you can argue that you understand the culture, the language, and the needs of the organization. But once you move out of that type of setting, your ground can get very shaky."

Physicians changing careers face another difficulty, one that is uncomfortable to address. Career consultant Celia Paul (referring to lawyers at the time) calls it an "entitlement mentality." (Others call it arrogance.) Some physicians have bought into society's view of their profession: that by virtue of their profession, they merit prestige, status, and a high income—and anything less is beneath them. But particularly if the physician is changing work cultures—from, say, a hospital to a corporation—such an attitude warrants adjustment. As Paul, quoted also in *Running From the Law,*[29] pointed out, people are hired because of their skills, not because of their titles, and "it's up to them to translate their skills into something marketable."

Another illusion physicians can fall under is the notion that because they've paid their dues in medicine, they'll never have to pay dues again. But if you're changing professions, that's just not true. "Don't expect employers to clamor for your services," says Arron.

Physicians are used to being recruited—even courted—with flowers, candy, and so on. To go out and convince other people to hire you can be a shock, particularly if you've never done it before. Physicians are used to being the star player, and they're used to playing the game according to certain rules. Search consultants who work with physicians are familiar with this difference. For example, if both a physician and a nonphysician in, say, Denver are interested in, say, an administrative position in Miami, and the search consultant contacts each of them to schedule a preliminary interview, usually the physician will expect the consultant to travel to him, while the nonphysician will not. The nonphysician will assume it's his responsibility to get to the consultant; he's playing by different rules—rules that physicians may be unaware of.

How can physicians adapt to this new playing field? Search consultants offer two suggestions: learn to think *organizationally,* and understand that the organization's needs are often urgent—that is, don't drag out the process unnecessarily; respond as promptly as you can to inquiries.

What to Tell Prospective Employers

Although this question perhaps puts the cart before the horse (you may not even be sure you'll be looking for a new employer, let alone thinking about what to tell one), it's worth thinking about now, early on. How should you handle prospective employers' questions about your decision to change careers? Arron's[30] advice to lawyers is again appropriate for physicians: Be very clear about your reasons for leaving the profession—both in your mind and in explaining them to potential employers. Then play up the work experience that's applicable to the targeted job, and play down what is not. Do not play *doctor* at all.

Since many people can't imagine why anyone would want to give up being a doctor, you have to tell them what your decision is based on—in a positive way. "Talk about what you're going to do next," Celia Paul advised. "For example, if you're interested in doing policy work on health issues, say that you want to build on what you've learned and do work that has more of a global impact than working with just individual patients."

You don't complain about your old position, "and you don't say you hate patients," Paul added. Instead, focus on the future and stay upbeat. For a time Paul taught a course at New York University on career alternatives for physicians. "Once I was teaching the class," she said, "and I asked, 'What's wrong with medicine?' They said, 'The patients,' and we all laughed. Well, people would not think that was funny if you were talking to them in a job interview."

Taking It Slow

It's essential to do an adequate amount of assessment work before making a career change. What's the best way of going about your self-assessment? Some people can do it through a workbook, but most people need interaction with someone; they need either a career workshop or a career counselor. It's hard to sit down in a room by yourself and do this sort of thing. Although many people are changing careers these days, it's one thing to read about them and it's another thing to be in a group where people listen to you and say, "I understand." The purpose of a career counselor or group is to help you to:

- Develop and maintain your focus

- Translate the skills you have developed in your current profession into skills you can use where you choose to go next

- Enhance your ability to handle change

- Find support during the emotional roller coaster

- Celebrate your success

In the process, you'll learn a lot about yourself, and you'll get an opportunity to look back at your life.

Gigi Hirsch says that one of the purposes of career counseling for physicians is to "give them the opportunity to be confused, and to get their confusion on the table" so that it can be worked through. Physicians, by culture and training, place a high value on *not* being confused. Part of Hirsch's job is to help them to define the problems. She reports that some physicians need no more career counseling than that. "Just by thinking about it in a systematic way, they were able to answer their own questions," she says.

The assessment process is not only important—it also takes time. Many physicians want to jump ahead to the question, What do I do? What do I do? "For most people, making a significant career change is a process that takes a while. It unfolds over a couple of years or so," says Gigi Hirsch. Celia Paul adds, "If doctors thoroughly work through the process, that will give them the better decision later." Arlene Hirsch told the *Chicago Tribune,* [31] "To people who are thinking of changing careers, I would say the first question you have to ask is 'Who am I?' Even before you look at the job, ask yourself what's important to you. Look inside yourself for answers and then, later, start to get information about the job market and tie it all together."

So put away your curriculum vitae for now—it's not time to revise it. It's time to reflect. Until you find your career counselor, career workshop, or support group, here are some questions to get your thinking started, and to begin the process of clarifying your goals.

(*Note:* Don't try to answer these questions at one sitting—or even in one day. After reading them over, make a date with yourself every day for the next two weeks to reflect on and write about them. And from now until you find your new job, set aside an hour a day, if you can, not only for reflecting but also for researching, calling other people, and setting up appointments related to your self-assessment/job search. The process takes months—even years—and it requires patience and persistence.)

What Makes You Tick? A Values Assessment

1. What's important to you? (Intellectual stimulation? Peace and quiet? Feeling that your work is socially useful? A high income? Helping others? Job security? Maintaining your current lifestyle? Expressing yourself creatively? Autonomy? Spending time with your family? Recognition as an expert? Working in a congenial atmosphere?...)

_____

_____

_____

_____

_____

2. Why do you work?

_____

_____

_____

_____

_____

3. What are you really after in life?

_____

_____

_____

_____

_____

4. What gives you satisfaction?

_____
_____
_____
_____
_____

5. What do you want and need at this point in your life?

_____
_____
_____
_____
_____

6. What do you care about?

_____
_____
_____
_____
_____

7. What are your priorities as a physician?

_____
_____
_____
_____
_____

8. What are your goals as an individual? If you're part of a couple, what are your goals as partners?

_____
_____
_____
_____
_____

9. How will your partner react if you decide to change professions?

_____

_____

_____

_____

_____

10. What are your ambitions?

_____

_____

_____

_____

_____

11. How have your standards of success changed since medical school?

_____

_____

_____

_____

_____

12. What's telling you now that you're not happy?

_____

_____

_____

_____

_____

13. On a separate piece of paper, write a brief summary (a half page or less) for each of the jobs you most enjoyed—and the jobs you most disliked.

_____

_____

_____

_____

_____

14. Think about the history of your career decisions. What were you looking for that you didn't find?

_____

_____

_____

_____

_____

15. Are the values you cherish the most being expressed at your current job?

_____

_____

_____

_____

_____

16. What price do you place on your happiness? What are you willing to give up to get what you say you want?

_____

_____

_____

_____

_____

Finding the Right Kind of Help

Career counselors come to the field out of different backgrounds (psychology, business, marketing, writing) and they use different approaches: some take a psychological approach while others take a more practical approach. It's important to choose a counselor who matches your style.

Career counselors do _not_ select your career and find you a job. Instead, they help you explore your values, assess your skills, and explore your options. It's important to choose one who understands the unique issues that physicians face, and one who displays no judgments about your choice to leave or stay in medicine. The best way to choose a service is to obtain references from other physicians.

What Do You Have to Offer?

What are your dreams for the future? What *can* you do and what do you *like* to do? The last half of that question is important—it's not just what we're able to do that's important, but what we *like* to do. Many of us have skills that we don't enjoy using—perhaps playing the piano. Or we enjoy using the skill now and then but wouldn't want to make a living doing it. It's a mistake to automatically jump from "If I can do this well..." to "then I should do it for a living."

Many of us were the victims of simplistic career counseling when we were young: "You're smart—you should be a doctor." Well, what if the thought of coping every day with sick people, hospital politics, and government regulations gives you hives?

When career counselors work one-on-one with clients, they usually instruct the clients to make a list of the things the clients have done that they're proud of—and from that list, skills are extrapolated. Physicians participating in a career workshop run by Celia Paul came up with this composite list of skills:

- Quick problem-solving abilities. When patients come into the office, the physician doesn't have all day to figure out what's wrong with them. And, of course, a physician working in an emergency room has to solve problems very quickly.

- High energy.

- Collaborating effectively with other professionals. For doctors to get the job done, it's very important in the hospital, particularly, that they work well with all the other professional people.

- Living with uncertainty and accepting the limits of what one can and can't do.

- Compulsiveness.

- Endurance.

- Selling/educating/persuading. Doctors have to persuade patients to follow the prescribed course of treatment—which is not always easy.

- Managing personnel.

- Managing a practice.

- Setting priorities among the many competing demands on one's time.

- Creating a team.

- Interviewing well. Doctors know how to ask the right kinds of questions and extract the necessary information, sometimes from people whose language and/or culture differs from their own.

- Writing clearly and persuasively.

- Speaking in public—the ability to educate the public about health and medicine.

- Decision making (perhaps without having 100% of the information, which takes courage).

- Manual dexterity.

- Assessing, analyzing, and using data.

- Handling a high level of responsibility.

- Advocating for patients.

- Nurturing and empathizing.

- Enlisting cooperation. "Think about how many people doctors have to cooperate with and coax along in order to get something done in a hospital," says Celia Paul. "Doctors depend on the people there to make something work."

Skills Inventory

1. List 10 to 15 things in your life that you're proud of (don't limit yourself to work accomplishments).

a. _____

_____

b. _____

_____

c. _____

_____

d. _____

_____

e. _____

_____

f. _____

_____

g. _____

_____

h. _____

_____

i. _____

j. _____

k. _____

l. _____

m. _____

n. _____

o. _____

2. On a separate piece of paper, write a brief narrative about each item on your list.

_____

_____

_____

_____

_____

3. Based on your 10 to 15 narratives, make a list of your skills and talents. (A career counselor might give you an extensive list to choose from: problem solving, making presentations, defining structure, administering, and so on. To get started, you may want to draw from the skills list, above.)

_____

_____

_____

_____

4. Look at your list of skills and talents in relation to what you've done as a physician in the last 5 years. What do you discover?

_____

_____

_____

_____

_____

5. Look at your list of skills and talents in relation to your current job. What do you discover?

_____

_____

_____

_____

_____

6. In what work situations have you felt the most stress and the least confidence? The least stress and the most confidence?

_____

_____

_____

_____

_____

Note: For those of you who skimmed these questions and now think you've completed the assessment part of the process, we offer this caution: working with a career counselor may be very challenging for you, because the counselor (a good one, at least) will *make* you answer these questions.

Additional Assessment Tools

Among the assessment tools used by career counselors are the Strong-Campbell Interest Inventory, which identifies interests, not aptitudes or personality traits; the Employee Aptitude Survey; and the Career Decision Maker, a program that tests interests and abilities. The Myers-Briggs Type Indicator (MBTI) is the granddaddy of the assessment tools; it's a personality evaluator that draws conclusions about preferences based on studies of four sets of character traits. To find a licensed MBTI administrator in your area, contact the national headquarters of the Association for Psychological Type, 9140 Ward Parkway, Kansas City, MO 64114, 816 444-3500. The membership chairperson will direct you to a local member or local chapter.

Finding New Life in an Old Career

Not every doctor who, out of frustration, considers leaving medicine will actually make the move. For many doctors, the solution to the problem of burnout is simply to get their practices fired up again.

Marketing your practice

By learning how to market their practices, physicians can breathe new life into what may have become a stale routine. Many physicians have been reluctant to market their practices because they equate marketing with hucksterism. It's not; it's simply letting people know about your availability. The old referral system that physicians could once count on is no longer in place, and today's consumer-conscious patients rely less on loyalty to a physician and more on cost-consciousness when making their decisions about medical care. If you want your practice to thrive, you've got to spread the word—and that can be accomplished in a dignified, professional way.

Chuck Woeppel is Vice President for Physician Marketing Services at Jackson and Coker, a physician-recruitment firm in Atlanta. He shows physicians how to practice their trade better, how to be better businesspeople, how to organize their offices better, and how to be more efficient and have a better quality of life.

"Physicians typically don't market their practices," Woeppel said in a telephone interview. "But they have wonderful mechanisms for marketing. Marketing for a physician is probably easier to do than for anybody else, because most of it is done by his or her current patients. But too often physicians don't provide their current patients with any way to market them."

How can physicians go about it? The strategies don't need to be complicated or involve a lot of time or money. "Many physicians now have a sign on their office wall that says, 'We appreciate your coming to see us, and we appreciate your telling your friends about us.' And then they make a brochure available that tells about themselves and their practice and what they do—and their patients take the brochure with them. I don't know about you," Woeppel added, "but whenever I've been to a physician who I thought was terrific, I've told other people about it. That's how most practices grow, as a matter of fact."

Public speaking (at the PTA, charity groups, or schools), publishing a practice newsletter, or teaching a short-term evening course for adults also can give a physician's practice a boost by increasing his or her visibility.

Revamping staffing patterns

When the physician gets a better handle on practice management, typically his or her quality of life improves significantly, Woeppel says. "A lot of times the problem is the staff the physicians have working for them: the staff is doing things for their own convenience rather than for the physician's convenience, and the physician is afraid to direct them. In those cases, I just recommend that they get an outside consultant to come in from time to time—maybe once a quarter—to take a look at the practice and make recommendations, and then implement those recommendations. The idea is to take the administration of long-term goals out of the physician's hands so that the administration of the day-to-day operations (which the physician definitely has to manage) is easier for him or her to do."

Managing expenses

Frequently a physician is not making enough money in his or her practice. The typical reason is that expenses are out of control. "Physicians have a tendency to have more people on their staff than they really need to have," Woeppel said. "By simply looking at the staffing program and the flow of patients, it's relatively easy to identify."

Simple practice-management techniques, such as finding competent office help and streamlining procedures so the physician's time is used more efficiently, can make a big difference, giving the physician time for other interests or for the rest he or she may need.

Management, Woeppel said, is the major reason physicians want to leave their practices. "Most of them enjoy practicing medicine," he explained. "But they find it laborious because of all the extraneous things they have to become involved in, such as governmental incursion, Medicare, the special reporting process they have to go through because of PSROs [now PROs], or one thing or another. And 99% of the time, those problems are easily fixed—by someone coming in, taking a look at the situation, and being objective about it."

Adjusting your schedule

For many physicians, their quality of life is diminished because they're killing themselves by the hours they work. "A lot of physicians have terrible hours of practice," Woeppel said. "What they do to themselves is sock it in to three or four days in order to take one extra day a week off. Well, if they want to take one extra day a week off, then they're going to have to think about lowering their income and not trying to sock five days of work into four days."

Another solution that eases burnout for some physicians is to reduce their practice hours to a more tolerable level and fill in those hours with work they enjoy more and/or are interested in exploring.

Professional practice-management consultants are also available. A subsidiary of the American Medical Association, AMA Financing & Practice Services, Inc, offers on-site practice management workshops for small groups (call 800 366-6968). The AMA offers several practice management publications (call 800 621-8335 for a catalog of offerings).

Considering a different kind of practice arrangement

Many physicians have responded to the economic pressures of managed care by changing their practice arrangements, often selling or merging their practices into larger organizations. There are several different practice arrangement options available for physicians today, including physician hospital organizations (PHOs), independent practice associations (IPAs), physician-owned HMOs, specialty care networks, multispecialty networks, and group practices without walls (GPWWs). In addition, physician practice management organizations (PPMs) offer their services to group practices. Each option has pros and cons; opinions differ among consultants and experts on which arrangements are most advantageous for physicians. Some believe, for instance, that PHOs have peaked in popularity.[32]

Never make a quick decision to sell or merge, even if you are feeling under pressure. Joining a large organization may not be right for you, warns business consultant Elaine Scheye (in *American Medical News*).[33] Weigh your personal circumstances, needs, and wants as well as your economic and professional goals. Take into account your own clinical style and the culture of your potential business associates. A qualified business or practice management consultant or attorney can help you determine which arrangement is best for you.

Watch *Medical Economics*, a semimonthly magazine, and *American Medical News*, a biweekly newspaper, for articles on practice management and new practice arrangements.

Changing specialties

Many physicians find job satisfaction by changing specialties. Perhaps, as medical students, they were among the 80% we cited earlier in the 1987 Glaxo study who felt they did not have adequate information about choosing a specialty. In 1995 Glaxo Wellcome surveyed practicing physicians about their specialties (2,561 physicians from 37 medical specialties participated).[34] The physicians were asked to identify the most and least appealing aspects of their work, and what advice they would offer students contemplating the specialty.

If you're dissatisfied with your current practice because it's too stressful, be aware of these specialties, which the respondents identified as *high-pressured:*

- Anesthesiology
- Cardiology
- Critical care medicine
- Emergency medicine
- Gastroenterology
- General surgery
- Hematology
- Infectious diseases
- Medical oncology
- Nephrology
- Neurological surgery
- Obstetrics and gynecology
- Pulmonary medicine
- Thoracic surgery

The survey participants judged these specialties to be *low to moderately pressured:*

- Dermatology

- Endocrinology and metabolism
- Neurology
- Nuclear medicine
- Ophthalmology
- Otolaryngology
- Physical medicine and rehabilitation
- Preventive medicine
- Rheumatology

Is your schedule the problem? Physicians in the following specialties said they tend to work *regular and predictable hours:*

- Adolescent medicine
- Allergy and immunology
- Colon and rectal surgery
- Dermatology
- Endocrinology and metabolism
- Geriatric medicine
- Nuclear medicine
- Ophthalmology
- Otolaryngology
- Pathology
- Physical medicine and rehabilitation
- Preventive medicine
- Psychiatry
- Rheumatology
- Sports medicine

Physicians in these specialties said they tend to work *irregular and/or long hours:*

- Cardiology
- Emergency medicine
- Gastroenterology
- General surgery
- Nephrology
- Neurological surgery
- Obstetrics and gynecology
- Orthopedic surgery
- Pulmonary medicine
- Thoracic surgery

Your schedule can depend in part on whether you are part of a group. In some specialties, physicians in large group settings worked fewer and/or more regular hours than solo physicians.

(The Glaxo Wellcome survey also asked physicians about 15 other critical aspects of their practice, including income, intellectual content, autonomy, security, and respect/approval from others.)

Reevaluating goals

If physicians are looking for a higher quality of life, it's essential that they look at their personal needs. Chuck Woeppel agrees: "They need to reevaluate themselves," he said. "Many times I'll tell physicians that it's a good idea for them to go see a psychologist and talk a little bit about where they want to be with their lives. They're trying to be all things to all people—and it doesn't work. It doesn't work in any other field, just as it doesn't work in being a doctor."

How Others May React to Your Career Change

Another aspect that makes the career-change process difficult for physicians is that some people simply will not understand why you want to change. What if a physician stops practicing medicine and, say, goes into pharmaceuticals marketing? How might his or her colleagues, parents, and family react? The career changer might encounter resistance, disbelief, or a brush-off: "So who expected to be happy in this life, anyway?" These assumptions and projections will have little or nothing to do with you as an individual and everything to do with society's expectations of physicians. (By mentioning them here we're certainly not endorsing them.)

We don't mean to disparage or underestimate the caring capabilities of anyone's family, friends, or colleagues; many career changers do indeed get the support they need. However, negative reactions are within the realm of possibility, and career changers will have an easier time coping with them if they don't come as a surprise. Some of the pain can be alleviated when problems are anticipated.

Patients

Patients may experience their physician's decision to stop practicing as psychological and physical abandonment. Their reaction, consciously or not, may be, *What do you mean you're not going to take care of me anymore?* They may, at some level, feel betrayed—and may express anger, directly or indirectly. This depends, of course, on the physician's specialty and how much ongoing contact he or she routinely has with patients. For example, a radiologist selling his or her practice would obviously have fewer patient reactions to cope with than a pediatrician would. Because patients have invested their faith in the physician, sometimes seeing the physician as a parental figure, the physician who breaks the relationship—and who doesn't fulfill the patients' expectations—is seen as breaching a trust.

In some ways, physicians are like priests in this society: once a priest, always a priest; and once a doctor, always a doctor. Both are assumed to be lifelong altruistic vocations—jobs that one doesn't stop doing unless...*what?* Although people don't quite say it, the assumption is that the priest (or doctor) somehow *wasn't good enough*—he or she couldn't cut it. Laypeople, on discovering there's an ex-priest in their midst, will stare hard, trying to fathom his "flaw."

Deborah L. Arron's career guide for lawyers, *Running From the Law: Why Good Lawyers Are Getting Out of the Legal Profession,*[35] attacks the myth of assumed incompetence right in its subtitle, by using the word *good*. The same is true of doctors, of course: perfectly capable physicians do indeed choose to get out of medicine. They would be wise, however, to anticipate such myths. Be prepared for assumptions and projections that have nothing to do with your actual capabilities, accomplishments, and motivations—and also be prepared for a feeling of isolation among people who aren't in the know.

If you plan to sell your practice, you'll want to give some thought to how you communicate that decision to your patients. For a discussion of handling patient relations when closing a practice, see "Tying Up the Loose Ends: Practice Transfer" in part 3.

Peers

When a physician decides to leave medical practice, peers may understand the stresses, but how they respond to this change—a change that has arisen out of your value system—depends on their value systems: are they people who, in general, support career changers? Or do their values tell them to stick with the program, no matter what? In addition to peers' genuine good wishes, it wouldn't be uncommon for them to experience feelings of abandonment and/or envy, depending on what the career changer is moving toward—or escaping from. Peers may feel left behind, stuck in all the problems you're escaping. They may feel uncomfortable, because your move will force them to reflect on their own situation, with all its pluses and minuses. You may find yourself kicking up a lot of dust in your personal relationships during your career change, because your departure from the group and from others' expectations forces everyone into a new relationship with you.

The way a peer group responds to someone leaving depends on how members of the group feel about that individual and the quality of their bond to that person, and also how they feel about people pursuing their own individual dreams.

Our hope is that anticipating these possible reactions from peers—and choosing not to take them personally—will help take the sting out of them if you ever encounter them.

Moving to part-time

Professionals who move from full-time to part-time (in order, for example, to spend more time with their children) may have to cope with an array of subtle negative reactions from their colleagues. Women in this situation face particular stresses. As Arlene Hirsch explained, "Any time a woman goes to part-time to try and balance career and family, I think that always generates some resentment from men or from other women who don't feel they have that so-called luxury. Again, their reactions are based on the idea of selfishness—that you're doing something for yourself that makes you look like you're not serious. The reason that women who work full-time rather than moving to part-time options feel resentful toward the part-timer and the stay-at-home moms so much is because they feel it affects their own credibility as professional women. Full-timers are afraid other people will use the example of part-timers as evidence that women aren't really serious about their careers. And people who work part-time complain that full-time people don't take them seriously."

Thus, the female physician moving to part-time may have a lot of reactions to detach from psychologically. As Hirsch put it, "There's an extra set of baggage put on women's decisions. Men don't have the expectation that they'll go in and out of the work force. Whereas women, because of the additional childbearing responsibilities, expect that they're going to take time out or at least have to adjust their priorities. They anticipate it, whereas men don't."

What sorts of reactions might a physician-father encounter if he decided to go to part-time to take care of his children? "Disbelief," Hirsch said. "A lack of understanding; but people would be less apt to assume he's not serious about his career. The man who stays home with his kid would be seen as a wimp—*unless* he was a single father. Then he'd probably be seen as heroic.

"For women in this society, being heroic means staying in the work force and taking care of both your career and your children; but if you take time out, you're a wimp," she continued. "Different standards. A female physician who decides she doesn't want to practice medicine anymore would run the risk of looking like she wasn't tough enough. People might not assume a male physician wasn't tough enough—but they might assume he wasn't successful enough."

Whatever your gender or situation, coping with others' reactions to your career change will take self-confidence, tolerance, detachment, and patience.

Parents

The parents of physicians often have an enormous emotional and financial stake in their children's choice of careers. Over the years they've invested time, love, and money, and they may even have footed the bill for their child's medical education. They derive status from their son's or daughter's position in life, and they have their own expectations of what their child's future will be. Out of sincere concern for their child's well-being, some may have a difficult time with the career change.

Spouse and children

Marilyn Moats Kennedy, the founder and managing partner of Career Strategies in Wilmette, Illinois, has counseled hundreds of physician career changers. In an article in *Group Practice Journal,*[36] she stressed that the physician's spouse and children *must* be part of the planning process if the physician wants his or her career change to be successful. Since the spouse and children will live with the consequences (financially, socially, and psychologically), the physician and his or her family must be treated as a unit when planning the change. This strategy is not just one of simple consideration for others; it's to ensure success. While the physician considers his or her options, the family members need to have an opportunity to look at theirs.

The physician's spouse and children derive status and even some of their identity from the physician's place in life. They have their own investment in the physician's work. Their lifestyle and their relationships with others may be affected by the change. Although you might not think your status has changed because you're now a physician executive instead of a practicing physician, your family will sense the difference. "Are you still a doctor?" your child might ask. "My friends said you weren't." Although physicians have been somewhat devalued in recent years and are seen as not quite the "MDeities" they used to be, being a physician is still the job with the highest status in our society. And practicing physicians are higher on the pecking order than nonpracticing ones, regardless of the importance of the nonpracticing MD's work. The physician's change from practicing to nonpracticing and the change in deference accorded him or her can shake up a family's self-image—if they let it. Kennedy recommends laughing off other people's reactions, if you can manage it. Don't let it eat away at family pride.

The financial implications of the change, whether the family's income goes up or down, may, of course, directly affect family members. They should, at the very least, be part of the discussion about the change. If the family income will decrease with the change, the spouse and children need to explore how they feel about a cut. Many family members may feel angry: trying to be noble and supportive is one thing; paying bills with less money is quite another. But in Kennedy's experience, even when a family experiences a significant reduction in income—"say from $200,000 to $85,000"—the change affected "quantity, not quality. For example, instead of 10 mini-vacations a year at expensive resorts and with first-class air travel (a tremendously overpriced treat), the family takes a longer vacation to a more moderately priced resort and everyone gets SuperSaver tickets." The family needs to be behind the change from the outset; otherwise, every spending cutback will feel like a deprivation rather than a choice.

The physician's spouse may *want* to be supportive about the career change, but he or she may feel threatened by other issues, such as the fear that the physician's move away from medicine may also somehow mean a move away from the family. The physician, now working in, say, an advertising agency instead of a hospital, or an executive suite instead of a lab, may meet new people who (the spouse fears) will somehow threaten the marriage and family lifestyle. Plus, if there's a drop in family income, a nonworking spouse can feel enormously stressed by the pressure to begin contributing right away to the family's income. If the spouse decides to return to work, he or she also needs and deserves competent career-planning help.

Physicians who leave practice to pursue other interests shouldn't be surprised when their status within the family changes, Kennedy warns. If you're no longer making $250,000 a year, your family's expectations of you may change. The balance of power within the family can take a definite shift—a topic that few family members want to look at, let alone talk about. The physician may be expected to "pitch in" more around the house, says Kennedy. One woman told her, "Why shouldn't he? He's not working 90 hours a week anymore."

Some people use their busy careers as a way of avoiding issues within their families. For them, more time at home—or just the change in general—may mean having to confront some issues they've tried to set aside. Change stirs the pot; new issues are sure to bubble up. It can be a time of stress—and also growth. Medicine is a clearly identifiable profession that comes complete with a professional identity that others can recognize. Being a doctor has a ring of authority that makes others take notice. Because this kind of recognition is hard to find in other professions, it can be equally hard to leave behind.

Kennedy offers these tips for ensuring a successful change:

- **Physicians and their families must be treated as a unit in career planning.** Competent help is essential. It's not psychological counseling that's needed so much as information from someone familiar with the process. This will reinforce the family's commitment to change. This has a very affirming effect, especially if the nonmedical spouse is simultaneously changing careers. The spouse becomes a full participant and begins to focus attention on his or her own life, working as an individual, rather than remaining a helpless bystander while someone else is the main event.

- **Involve the whole family in every step and decision. You'll save pain, time, and money.** Children have valid, deeply held convictions. A city child may learn to adapt to a small town, but shouldn't he or she be asked beforehand what in the present environment is especially precious? When the parent's career change involves a physical move, that child's interests (whether it's horseback riding, pottery, or a school with a winning basketball team) should be part of the family's shopping list for a new community. Ignoring the family's interests and needs is sure to cause enormous problems down the road.

Whether or not the family moves, the nonworking spouse needs to consider his or her needs and do his or her own life-work planning. It's wrong to assume that nothing will change just because the family isn't moving anywhere; if the physician changes careers and enters a new work culture, in a sense his or her spouse also has a new job.

- **Talk about values.** What is your family all about? What are they interested in? What do they want to improve during this period of change?

For example, the family of one of Kennedy's clients, a psychiatrist, agreed that Wednesday would be family night. Even though the father would be traveling some of the time, Wednesday would be the one night in the week he'd try to be in town. A fancy dinner on their best china once a week was their way of affirming the family's importance.

- **Bring each family member's hidden agenda to the surface.** Encourage family members to talk about the effects of the change and their feelings about it— what will be new, what they think they'll miss, and other changes they anticipate. *Nothing softens the effect of change like a head-on assault.* In a family environment in which it's safe to admit, "I miss flying to Hawaii first-class," people can talk about the vacations they *want* to take. A trip to the Bahamas, perhaps?

Family members need a decent period of mourning, too, Kennedy adds. Nothing prolongs a family's adjustment to change as much as the attitude that everyone should be "brave." Leave that to professional soldiers. Families should vent their disappointments as well as celebrate their triumphs. This process will also diminish the career changer's guilt.

- **Plan, organize, and set deadlines for any planned change.** While it is not always possible to chart the course of a career change from the beginning, it is best to develop a plan as soon as possible. Try to avoid keeping your family in limbo for months on end. When you announce your career change to your family, they will find it easier to handle if you already have a transition plan in place. Draw up a timetable for assessing skills, environments, and job possibilities, and include a target date for the change and/or move. If the family can see a written plan of what is to occur and when—with suitable time-outs for holidays and vacations—they can be part of the process and avoid feeling isolated, powerless, and afraid. After all, the master plan, of which they are part, is posted on the refrigerator door for all to see. Don't underestimate the importance of something concrete to reassure and rally the family—it makes an enormous difference.

Remember, it's one thing to announce, "I'm unhappy as a pathologist. I want to do something else," thereby raising a host of questions and anxieties for the family. It's another to state, "I'm unhappy, I want to change. Here's my plan."

To sum up, changing careers can be exhilarating, terrifying, threatening, painful, and disruptive. So why bother? Why go through all of this career-exploration business if the decisions are so difficult and it's so stressful and complicated? We asked career consultant Arlene Hirsch. Her straightforward reply: "Potential happiness."

It reminded us of the old story about the guy who was thinking about going back to school and switching careers.

"Should I do it?" he asked a friend. "After all, I'll be 45 when I get out of school!"

"So? You'll be 45 anyway," the friend replied. "And at 45, you might as well be doing something you like."

Career and Life Planning Resources

The Center for Physician Development
1 Memorial Dr, 15th Floor
Cambridge, MA 02142
617 252-0241

Center for Professional Well-Being
21 W Colony Place, Suite 150
Durham, NC 27705
919 489-9167

The American College of Physician Executives
Career Choices Program
4890 W Kennedy Blvd, Suite 200
Tampa, FL 33609-2575
800 562-8088

Notes to Part 1

1. Crane M. Thinking about leaving practice? Read this first. *Medical Economics.* August 15, 1988:132-136.

2. Ibid.

3. Hirsch G. Health care reform and physician stress. *Physician Executive.* February 1996:31-32.

4. Curry W, ed. *Roads to Medical Management: Physician Executives' Career Decisions.* Tampa, Fla: American Academy of Medical Directors; 1988:68-73.

5. Ibid, 23-29.

6. Steptoe S. Dispirited doctors: hassles and red tape destroy joy of the job for many physicians. *Wall Street Journal.* April 10, 1987:1.

7. Wassersug J. It's just no fun anymore. *Private Practice.* December 1985;17:34.

8. Steptoe.

9. American Medical Association. *Principles of Managed Care: A Summary of American Medical Association Policy.* Chicago, Ill: American Medical Association; 1993.

10. Terry K. Forecast for doctors: stronger winds of change. *Medical Economics.* December 11, 1995:161.

11. Hymowitz C, Pollock EJ. Psychobattle. *Wall Street Journal.* July 13, 1995:A1.

12. Johnsson J. HMOs dominate, shape the market. *American Medical News.* January 22/29, 1996:1.

13. Castro J. Who owns the patient anyway? *Time.* July 18, 1994:48.

14. Morain C. When managed care takes over, watch out! *Medical Economics.* October 12, 1995:38.

15. Himmelstein DU, Lewontin JP, Woolhandler S. Who administers? Who cares? Administrative and clinical employment in the United States and Canada. *American Journal of Public Health.* February 1996:172.

16. Pascual P. California doctors say managed care erodes income, quality of care. *The Business Press* (via Knight-Ridder/Tribune). May 1, 1996.

17. Carton B. What's up, Doc? Stress and counseling. *Wall Street Journal.* January 6, 1995:B1.

18. Crane.

19. Terry.

20. Wassersug.

21. American Medical Association Center for Health Policy Research. *Socioeconomic Characteristics of Medical Practice 1995.* Chicago, Ill: American Medical Association; 1995:112.

22. Mitka M. Doctor pay shrinks for first time in '94. *American Medical News.* January 22-29, 1996:1.

23. Fikes BJ. Oh, doctor! Caught in a maelstrom of reform. *San Diego Business Journal.* October 23, 1995:sec 1, p17.

24. Prager LO. Gatekeepers on trial. *American Medical News.* February 12, 1996:1.

25. Weiss B. Managed care: there's no stopping it now. *Medical Economics.* March 13, 1995:33.

26. McIlrath S, Mitka M. Putting the brakes on physician supply. *American Medical News.* February 12, 1996:1.

27. Glaxo Inc. *Nationwide Survey of Medical Students 1987.* Research Triangle Park, NC: Glaxo Inc; 1987.

28. Arron DL. *Running From the Law: Why Good Lawyers Are Getting Out of the Legal Profession.* Berkeley, Calif: Ten Speed Press; 1991. Quoted by permission.

29. Ibid.

30. Ibid.

31. Libman N. First person: I'm helping people discover for themselves what they can do (interview with Arlene S. Hirsch). *Chicago Tribune Magazine.* July 8, 1990:28.

32. Terry, 161.

33. Larkin H. There's more than one way to organize. *American Medical News.* February 12, 1996:21.

34. Glaxo Wellcome Inc. *Specialty Profiles.* 3rd ed. Research Triangle Park, NC: Glaxo Wellcome Inc; 1996.

35. Arron.

36. Kennedy MM. Making a move and keeping your family, too. *Group Practice Journal.* September/October 1985:72-76. Excerpted with permission of the American Group Practice Association.

Part 2
Nonclinical Career Opportunities for Physicians

How Wide Is the Nonclinical Universe?

The short answer to that question is this: It's wide—and getting wider. Although the vast majority (90%) of today's physicians are involved in patient care, there is great diversity in career paths among the remaining 10%.

What are all those nonclinicians doing? While we don't have a complete picture, we do have some ideas, gleaned from anecdotes offered by career consultants and search firms, and from the research of others. Career counselors report that physicians are finding nonclinical employment in the following fields/areas/roles:

- Public relations. Many PR firms serve the field of medicine or its allied industries. (In fact, Burson-Marsteller, a firm serving the pharmaceutical industry, used to widely publicize the fact that it employed Dr. Arthur Hull Hayes, Jr., the former FDA commissioner, as a consultant.[1])

- Medical publishing—trade journals, books, abstracts, newsletters.

- Media consultants or reporters on medical issues. Appearing on radio and TV talk shows is an effective way for a physician to build his or her medical practice; some doctors, however, are able to make a full-time career out of medical education for the public.

- Copywriting for advertising agencies. Many ad agencies need people who can write copy that appeals to doctors and others in the medical community. The ad agencies' clients include HMOs, private health care, and pharmaceutical manufacturers.

- Doctors-turned-writers. There are dozens of these, including the novelist/filmmaker Michael Crichton and psychiatrists Robert Coles and Oliver Sacks.

- Heading up corporate medical departments.

- Consultants to law firms, insurance companies, or similar organizations. Performed on a per diem basis or through a retainer arrangement, part-time consulting can be a low-risk way of exploring other work environments and broadening one's network.

- Program analysts or policy planners—at a private foundation or for a government group, such as the National Institutes of Health.

- Investment banking. One physician/banker's job is to analyze companies that produce high-tech medical products. According to a career consultant, this is a hot area, one in which tremendous amounts of money can be made.

- Securities analysts. Physicians evaluate pharmaceutical firms or hospital chains for stock firms.

- Hospital administration/private health-care administration.

- Sales of medical equipment. As employees of large medical-wares suppliers, like Baxter, physicians sell very sophisticated technical equipment to other physicians.

- Sales of private health-care programs.

- Quality assurance. This a good area for doctors who want to cut back on their schedules, because they can work at it part-time.

- Accreditation—being part of the team that evaluates hospitals.

- Peer-review panelists.

- Disability determination. A psychiatrist who works part-time for the federal government reviewing charts for people applying for disability benefits enjoys the flexible hours. And if she ever decides to quit her regular full-time job, she knows she'll have at least some income while she's looking.

  Richard Harris, a Chicago psychiatrist in full-time private practice since 1982, spends 4 hours every other week reviewing charts in disability cases and consulting with staff at an insurance company. Harris appreciates the change of pace that his consulting position brings. Much of his regular practice involves psychoanalysis, a slow and painstaking process. At the insurance company, he can assess a problem situation fairly quickly. He also likes the change of environment. "I like interfacing with the greater world, outside of the confines of my office," Harris said in a phone interview.

- Computer-system developers.

- Deans of medical schools.

- Staff physicians to advertising agencies. The physician's job is to watch for potential problems with the Food and Drug Administration (FDA) and offer advice on specific medical problems.

- Real-estate developers. A lot of physicians are doing this, according to Chuck Woeppel of Jackson and Coker. They start by working with hospitals and see the opportunity to develop medical-office buildings and research facilities. Some start part-time and, when it grows large enough, jump into it full-time. "I would say that at every hospital in the country you'll find at least one of these people." For example, one physician has developed magnetic resonance imaging in several dozen locations, Woeppel said; another develops ophthalmological surgical centers around the country; yet another develops ENT surgical centers. And how much money is there to be made? "The average real-estate-developing physician, I would think, is definitely a millionaire," said Woeppel.

Is that all? you may be asking. *Do I only have two dozen options?*

In part 1 we speculated that many of today's dissatisfied physicians suffered as medical students or residents from a lack of good career information. Martin D. Keller, MD, PhD, chairman of the Department of Preventive Medicine at Ohio State University, reports that the information medical students receive today about their career options is still woefully inadequate. "In residency, they're exposed to only a very narrow band of clinical specialties and to virtually nothing nonclinical," he told us. "This restricts their horizons terribly."

In response to this need, Keller and his colleague, T. Donald Rucker, PhD, published *Careers in Medicine:* Traditional and Alternative Opportunities[2] in 1986 (revised in 1990), which included a study of nonclinical job titles. How wide was the nonclinical universe in 1986? Keller and Rucker unearthed more than *900* job titles—a number that has certainly risen in the ensuing years.

They discovered some of what you might expect: MDs working as executive VPs of quality control (in pharmaceuticals manufacturing), associate deans of alumni affairs (in medical schools), directors of ethics advisory boards (at NIH), and health officers (for USAID)—and some of what you might not: members of the U.S. House of Representatives, commanders in chief (for the Pacific Fleet), and mayors (of Coos Bay, Oregon). They also found numerous presidents (of a major oil company, a publishing company, the Flying Physicians Association, and baseball's American League). They even found a magician (part-time).

The recent rapid changes in medicine, and the many organizations that have sprung up around the nonclinical fields, have given Keller and his colleagues an idea. "Perhaps it's time for an offshoot of the American Board of Medical Specialties," he said recently, "one that addresses the many nonclinical medical specialties. Perhaps an 'American Board of Nonclinical Medical Specialties'?"

Because we think it's important to have a full sense of the diversity of options, we've included Rucker and Keller's multipage study as appendix 2. The job titles, divided into 14 categories, "all...depict positions that differ significantly from those of traditional medical practice," Rucker and Keller note. Their search focused on jobs "where at least 80% of the physician's time was probably devoted to duties other than direct patient care."

Rucker and Keller compiled their information through a process Rucker describes as "haphazard incrementalism": for 2 ½ years he saved everything that crossed his desk that mentioned an MD in a nonclinical role. The sources included numerous periodicals, newsletters, directories, and related references. "Since the source material did not cover the entire universe, or purport to be representative," Rucker and Keller caution, "our examples should be approached as guideposts for career exploration and not as a road map that specifies every choice that may appear on your journey. Moreover, additional career options may be found as doctors create their own businesses and assume positions never held previously by a physician."

Rucker and Keller note the study's limitations, which include a bias toward executive positions and some duplication of titles with similar responsibilities. "In cases where minimum numbers could be established, a figure is reported as a suffix to the entry, viz, 'Publishing, Editor (33).'"

"Finally," they add, "certain positions may require special experience and/or additional training beyond the standard medical residency program"; for example, a dual doctorate (MD/PhD) may be required for some teaching or research positions, and "a master's degree in public health or business administration may be mandated by some employers."

Let's take a closer look at a few nonclinical pursuits for physicians. Judging by the amount of press they receive (and by the membership of their related organizations), they're among the most popular these days.

Physician Executives

"Doctors are lousy managers." You hear it everywhere; it has become the conventional wisdom about MDs. (To the extent that the notion is true, perhaps the blame can rest with medical-school curricula, which typically include little or no management training.) But perhaps the real reason behind the recent explosion in the number of physician managers is revenge: physicians, tired of having their management skills maligned, are excelling in the executive suite—and proving the conventional wisdom wrong.

Why do physicians become physician executives? For much the same reasons that physicians consider leaving regular practice, as outlined in part 1, except that the pull factors are more important than the push factors, according to a 1994 survey conducted for the American College of Physician Executives.[3] While negative factors such as stress and dissatisfaction were considerations, the most common reasons given for becoming a physician executive were an attraction to management and a desire to make a positive impact on health care.

What exactly do physician executives do? There's no single definition. Because medical management (or "administrative medicine") is still a new profession, there are few clear-cut descriptions, although there is similarity in roles and responsibilities. Physician executives' job titles cover a wide range—from chief executive officer to assistant medical director to vice president of business development and others.

Additional training

Does a physician who wants to become a physician manager need an MBA? Most physician executives we've read about have sought out management training of one sort or another. Some went full-time for their MBAs, while others met their educational needs through weekend courses, summer workshops, and management-training seminars. Nearly every large university offers these kinds of programs during the summer and/or at night, reports one physician recruiter. Harvard's annual program on "Leadership for Physician Executives" is "wonderful," he claims (see address, page 58). Students can combine a medical and business education in joint degree programs, now offered at over two dozen schools in the US.[4]

In the 1994 ACPE survey, 43% of the physicians responding had MBAs and 22% had MPHs. Three percent had MHAs, 5% had JDs, and 27% had other degrees.[5]

Mark Saberman, Senior Vice President for Medical Affairs at the John Muir Medical Foundation, a California IPA, believes that you don't necessarily need an MBA to be a physician executive, but you do need to be conversant with health law, public policy, and insurance terminology. Although an MBA is helpful, it isn't everything. "If you become a medical director in an HMO or other kind of provider organization, you will still be called upon to know much more than you can get out of an MBA," says Saberman. He recommends that physicians entering into management take upper-level college courses in law, negotiating, and administration. Most organizations require that a physician executive have at least 5 years of clinical practice, but do not require an MBA. "In the future, an MBA may likely be a required credential on your resume," adds Saberman. "Right now it's not essential."

Current trends in the health-care-executive arena

The rush toward managed health care is creating a need for physician managers, according to David R. Kirschman, president of the Physician Executive Management Center, a Tampa, Florida, physician executive search firm. "The bad news about managed care," says Kirschman, "is that it is changing every-thing. The good news about managed care is that there are more and more op-portunities for physician executives." Managed health care operations are looking to physicians to provide the needed expertise and leadership in man-agement roles.

Mike Doody, a partner in the health-care-executive search firm of Kieffer, Ford and Hadelman in Oak Brook, Illinois, agrees. "I think we're going to see an in-creasing number of physicians in administrative positions—not necessarily in the number one, CEO, position—but as the VP for medical affairs, as medical director, as chief of the department, as directors of insurance companies, and so on. I think there's going to be more of those, because we're seeing a conver-gence between the financing of health care and the quality of health care. It's becoming more closely meshed, and much more complex."

Physician-executive salaries

We asked search consultant Doody how a physician's income changes when he or she goes from practicing to administration—a difficult question, since there's a wide range of incomes within each position. Doody pointed out that they are different career tracks, and thus hard to compare. "Obviously," he added, "most people aren't interested in changing careers and significantly al-tering their lifestyles. But of the many physicians who are moving into these positions out of practice (*not* the guys who decided early in medical school that their career track was going to be in administrative medicine as opposed to medical practice, but the guys who've been in practice who decide to make the career change), there are a number of them that do it later rather than earlier. And some of them do it, perhaps, after their peak expense years are past them: their kids are mostly raised and are finished with school, and so on.

"Their income needs," Doody continued, "are not as significant as when their outgo needs were high. So the physicians can now take a job for less because they don't have the demand, or they have already built their nest egg."

"I would say that typically you're going to find [physician executives] in the $200,000 to $250,000 range," said Chuck Woeppel, Vice President for Physician Marketing Services at Jackson and Coker, a physician-recruitment firm in Atlanta.

The other side of the financial story, Doody explained, is that sometimes the physicians are able to combine their administrative position with a part-time practice. This situation offers the physician managers two benefits: they have the opportunity for some modest additional income and they keep their clinical skills sharp.

The Physician Executive Management Center, Tampa, Florida, has been surveying physician executives about their compensation packages for over ten years. According to David R. Kirschman, president of the organization, "The salaries and incentives for senior physician executives (Medical Director or Vice President of Medical Affairs [VPMAs]) in hospitals vary by size of institution. Median total compensation (salary plus incentives) in 1995 for smaller hospitals (100 to 349 beds) was $167,200 and in larger hospitals (500+ beds), $186,000. These numbers have increased over past years at a rate of 4% to 8%, mostly reflecting cost of living changes. Fringe benefits continue to be about 20% to 25% of base compensation and typically include health, dental, life and disability plans, CME time and expenses, journals and dues for professional organizations."

Kirschman notes that physicians in the higher-income specialties are usually disappointed to learn about the salary ranges of hospital medical directors/ VPMAs. "Physicians need to understand the concept that salaries are pegged to the value of the position and negotiations with individual candidates start there. A hospital cannot and should not pay an orthopedic surgeon, for example, more as its Medical Director than it would pay a pediatrician in the same job."

Can you mix a nonclinical career with a medical practice?

"It depends," Woeppel told us. "Many of the physicians [who've gone into business] stay part-time in their medical practices. But they realize very quickly that if they become proficient at it they may have to leave their medical practice, depending on which one they want more, practicing medicine or going into business. And typically, they will go into this kind of business because it's very lucrative—much more lucrative than their medical practices."

Some mix a full-time clinical career with a lucrative sideline. "It's possible," said Woeppel, "depending on the people you have working for you." One plastic surgeon developed a very sophisticated computer system that's being sold to hospitals. He practices full-time while being fully in charge of his company.

Many physician executives successfully maintain a part-time practice, reported Woeppel. One physician, the longtime medical director of a large medical staff, was able to maintain a 2-day-a-week practice in internal medicine for 20 years;

recently, though, he gave up the practice to devote all his time to the administrative medicine he enjoys.

Although some physician managers no longer practice, some argue that physician managers must keep their clinical skills up-to-date to (1) remain in touch with the issues facing the physicians the managers are supervising and (2) maintain their credibility with their colleagues. Indeed, some health-care organizations insist that the physician managers in their employ practice part-time.

Mike Doody spelled out some of the reasons that a physician executive—say, a hospital CEO—would decide to continue practicing part-time. First, as we just mentioned, is the issue of credibility. The 57-year-old physician administrator, for example, perceives an erosion of belief in his clinical skills among his 30- and 35-year-old colleagues. It may be only a perception, not reality, but it affects him nonetheless.

For other physician executives, the decision to practice part-time comes simply out of a desire to not lose the skills they worked so hard to acquire. They say to themselves, Even though I want to move to another area, I don't want to totally abandon my practice.

"But there's a very practical issue that comes to play if the doctor wants to carry on a part-time medical practice," Doody told us, "[which is] a possible conflict of interest." Doody offered this example: Let's say the new CEO at a hospital happens to be a surgeon. Surgeons depend on referrals from other physicians. If the surgeon plans to practice surgery, say, 1 day a week, one could argue ("and," said Doody, "argue with a lot of logic") that such an arrangement would disrupt relationships and breed mistrust among the other surgeons (and between the CEO and the surgeons). The other surgeons may wonder if they're expected to give the CEO more referrals, since he now has some power over them and can affect their privileges at the hospital. Or perhaps, based on their assessment of the CEO's surgical skills, the other surgeons *don't* make any additional referrals to him. The first time the surgeon/CEO makes a decision in favor of one doctor over the other, will they mistrust his reasons? Will they wonder if his decision was influenced by who sent him referrals? "You've got to be very careful about that," Doody said.

Another potential conflict could come up when the surgeon/CEO and the other surgeons schedule their times in the OR. "Who gets the early times and who gets the late times" can be a big issue, Doody explained. "The OR supervisor who does the scheduling of surgeries [would be put in an awkward position]. Who's the guy that signs your paycheck?" Doody said. "It's the president of the hospital, who just happens to be a surgeon. And is the OR supervisor going to give him preferential treatment over the other surgeons?"

What specialties would be less apt to run into such a conflict? "Perhaps if [the physician executive was] a dermatologist, and maybe the only one on staff," Doody said. "Or if you were a specialist in infectious diseases, and it was a hospital that wasn't large enough to have more than one. Or maybe you're a family practitioner, or an internist with a very limited practice, or maybe it's only a clinical practice—there are various ways to skin that cat," he added. "But it's another set of problems or issues that have to be attended to when you're talking about physicians in executive positions."

Resources for information on physician executives

The American College of Physician Executives
(11,000 members)
4890 W Kennedy Blvd, Suite 200
Tampa, FL 33609
813 287-2000; 800 562-8088
e-mail: wwwacpe@acpe.org
web page: http://www.acpe.org/home.html

A good source of information for what's going on in the burgeoning field of medical management and physician executives is *Physician Executive Journal of Management,* published monthly by the American College of Physician Executives. The ACPE also publishes several books of interest for the physician who is considering management, including *Fundamentals of Medical Management: A Guide for the Physician Executive,* edited by Jerry L. Hammon, MD, FACPE; and *New Leadership in Health Care Management: The Physician Executive,* second edition.

The ACPE World Wide Web page (see "Using the Internet as a Career Resource," page 89) has listings of events and career opportunities.

American Medical Directors Association
(5,200 members)
10480 Little Patuxent Pkwy, Suite 760
Columbia, MD 21044
800 876-2632; 410 740-9743

"Leadership for Physician Executives: A Seminar for Health-Care
Administrators"
Harvard Medical School, Department of Continuing Education
PO Box 825
Boston, MA 02117
617 432-1525

Physician Executive Management Center
4014 Gunn Hwy, Suite 160
Tampa, FL 33624
813 963-1800

MDs in the Pharmaceutical Industry

Daniel L. Kisner, MD, is a former divisional vice president of a major pharmaceutical company. In a lengthy interview in 1989, with Joe Ann Jackson, who was then product manager, AMA Physicians Career Resource, he set the stage for our understanding of what the pharmaceutical industry has to offer MDs.

"Probably 10 years ago it wasn't fashionable for physicians to work for pharmaceutical companies," Kisner said. "Drug companies were almost part of the military industrial complex. There was all this anxiety about selling your soul to the company." But times have changed, Kisner explained. "What has happened in the last decade is a progressive trend toward legitimization of industry physicians. Some of our very best academic physicians in the country have gone into the pharmaceutical industry. They are now the role models for entering physicians and junior clinical physicians. The pharmaceutical industry does not hire losers in the industry," he continued. "They don't hire people who couldn't make it in academia. We are not the graveyard for discarded physicians."

One reason the industry has had an image problem, said Kisner, is that the average physician only meets the sales representatives who come to their offices to pester them, not the physicians working for the pharmaceutical companies. But "the days of the old attitude toward the industry are finished," Kisner said.

How are MDs employed in the pharmaceutical industry? According to Kisner, the range of activities for physicians in the industry is quite wide. "Much of what the pharmaceutical industry does," he explained, "is related to the development and clinical evaluation of new drugs. The industry spends its money, effort, and time on bringing new drugs to market. The program in which this development is done is run and staffed by physicians—many of [the programs] are for physicians—so that the range of activities, from the entry-level position to the vice president of clinical development, will be fairly wide."

Entry-level physicians are responsible for:

- Organizing clinical studies
- Recruiting investigators for the studies
- Writing research protocols
- Setting up and monitoring studies
- Analyzing the data from statisticians
- Writing reports
- Publishing the data

What kind of background would an entry-level physician need? Is there a certain specialty that would be best suited? "Physicians who are engaged in new drug development are, by and large, specialists," Kisner replied. "That is not to say that [a physician] couldn't learn what he or she needs about a field to do the work. But in general we try to hire internists, people who have internal medicine subspecialties. If a job is very heavily oriented toward a specialty, eg, cardiovascular, we would then try to hire a cardiologist.

"There is a wide need for expertise in the area of clinical pharmacology," Kisner added, "so that people trained in clinical pharmacology are sought after by the industry and certainly have the option to make their careers in industry. Clinical pharmacologists in industry can actually do clinical work as well as doing the studies themselves and monitoring the patients, as opposed to just organizing and supervising the research. By and large, other physicians who come into the industry can be administrators—research administrators, organizers—as opposed to doing the hands-on work themselves."

What's a typical day on the job for a physician in the pharmaceutical industry? An entry-level physician might:

- Travel to visit investigators
- Spend time in the office writing protocol and analyzing data
- Talk on the phone to investigators or opinion leaders in the research area

- Organize conferences
- Write budget proposals and development plans

The activities of the day vary, an aspect that attracts a lot of people to the industry, Kisner said. "You're not doing the same thing day in and day out."

Are most physicians in the pharmaceutical industry older or younger? "We have the whole gamut," said Kisner. "There is no preference for older or younger."

Is board certification a requirement? "No," said Kisner. "We try to hire people who are licensed. Beyond licensure, there are no hard-and-fast rules. Certification is a plus, of course. It depends on the goals of the organization and the goals of the company. They may not need a board-certified cardiologist to do some kinds of work, so they will tailor their recruitment to the level of experience and sophistication they need."

Once the physician is on the job, there's a lot he or she would have to learn: for example, how drug development is done, and what the FDA requirements are for research studies. "If they haven't been engaged in it before," said Kisner, "they would need to understand clinical study design, protocol development, and appropriate ways of analyzing and reporting data. Some physicians who come from a more academic environment are accustomed to writing research protocols and analyzing their data—and they may find it easier. Those who have never done that sort of thing have to learn that process."

What entry-level positions are generally available? Kisner mentioned three: clinical drug development, hands-on drug research, and medical support positions.

"Most companies have medical support positions for compounds already on the market," Kisner explained. "These are the people who answer phone calls, respond to queries from patients or physicians, and keep track of postmarketing toxicity surveys."

There are much higher entry levels as well, "depending on what people have done," Kisner said. "Somebody coming out of an academic environment, where they had done a lot of research and are accustomed to protocols, might come in at a more supervisory role." However, that's unusual, he said.

Bruce Herman, a physician recruiter with the Bruce Rogers Company in Port Washington, New York, seconds this. "Most pharmaceutical companies are trying to promote from within," says Herman, "so a lot of positions available are entry-level." Herman points out that there are now two tracks for physicians in pharmaceutical companies. One track is the traditional path of clinical research. Specialists are welcomed here, unlike other parts of the physician employment arena where generalists seem preferred. The second track involves interfacing with managed-care companies. Pharmaceutical companies need physicians with experience in managed-care settings to help them do business effectively with large HMOs. For these positions, a more general background, such as family practice, is appropriate.

What about salaries? According to Herman, a physician coming into a pharmaceutical company at an entry level should expect to make between $110,000 and $120,000 his or her first year. "And that's just base pay," Herman adds. "Depending on the company, you might get a bonus based on performance." Pharmaceutical companies also offer good health plans and a wide range of other fringe benefits, which physicians in private practice would have to pay for individually.

What is the work setting like? For an entry-level position, Kisner reports, it's usually an office with perhaps a secretary out front. "They may have some clinical monitor people reporting to them, maybe not." It depends on the company and what the physician does.

Do physicians in the pharmaceutical industry need people skills? Management skills? "A lot of physicians in medicine have supervised their office staff, or are accustomed to a very rigidly defined role-playing situation, sort of barking orders when things need to happen," Kisner said. "People who work in a business environment are not going to jump every time someone with an MD behind their name says something. It's much more important to be persuasive and skilled." If you are going to be supervising people, he added, it's also important "to understand and think a little about your impact on them. People skills are important.

"Management training is another issue. A person with good people skills and no previous management training can be trained to manage. They can be trained to supervise effectively, set goals, provide feedback (positive and negative), make the hard decisions, be rational, be calm, not be arbitrary, not be a dictator. You can teach people the most effective management style."

What do you look for on a résumé in terms of academic degrees? According to Kisner, although candidates don't need to have MBAs, the degree has its use. It helps, he said, if the person coming in the door "has a fairly good sense of what a market economy is, and how to manage people—which sometimes can be learned in business school.

"A drug company makes products," he went on. "It is also an industry where a physician can do scientifically challenging work that helps mankind and makes a real contribution to society, for which you are well paid. The company itself, no matter what its high ideals are, has to make money to survive. People in business, even if they are primarily clinicians or scientists, tend to have a pretty good grasp of that issue, and they know how to relate to the sales and marketing people; they know how to relate to the business people." As an entry-level physician, he pointed out, you may work for a non-MD, "so an MBA doesn't hurt."

Another good degree, according to Kisner, is a PhD in a basic science. "We're talking about 'scientific' PhDs," he clarified. "People who have degrees in addition to medicine tend to understand science a little better than doctors do. Physicians are not scientists, by and large. They have a very limited exposure to scientific theory, and many clinicians don't have much experience with the basic concepts of clinical research."

A lot of MD/PhDs come in with a better scientific understanding, Kisner asserts. "The additional spin-off is that they are also very valuable in relating to the 'bench researchers' who discover a drug. The MD/PhDs can talk to those people in their scientific area, whereas the average clinician cannot."

What advice would you offer to a physician coming into the pharmaceutical industry? "Put together a good résumé. Pay attention to how you interview. These jobs are competitive," he added. "I can interview three to four experienced industry physicians for every MD entry-level job that I have.

"From the time a drug falls out of a laboratory until the time it is filed with the FDA, the average cost spent by pharmaceutical companies per drug is one hundred million dollars ($100,000,000)." That much money is "not handed over to flunkies," Kisner said. "The drug development costs have become tremendously expensive. We need qualified people to run those programs. People who understand the research, know the medicine, know the clinical development questions that have to be answered, organize the studies, recruit the right kind of investigators, and produce quality data. It is far too expensive a process to turn over to anybody but high-quality people. The industry has been able to attract high-quality people to run these programs," Kisner concluded. "Participating in these programs is a very exciting way to make a living."

Resources for more information about MDs in the pharmaceutical industry

Schmidt R. The pharmaceutical physician—requirements for the position. *European Journal of Clinical Pharmacology.* 1991;41:387-391.

Shaw L. A misunderstood specialty: a survey of physicians in the pharmaceutical industry. *Journal of Clinical Pharmacology.* May 1991:419-422.

Spilker B. Career opportunities for physicians in the pharmaceutical industry. *Journal of Clinical Pharmacology.* 1989;29:1069-1076.

MDs in Law

Why are MDs drawn to the law? Perhaps it's the perception that lawyers have better hours and earn bigger incomes for less work, or perhaps it's the opportunity to protect other MDs from unjust malpractice attacks. Some physicians get a law degree because they realize that in order to continue doing what they're doing (such as running a large group practice) and do it *well,* they need legal knowledge. Other, more combative types may be just looking for a good fight.

Lee S. Goldsmith, MD, LLB, is clear about his reasons for getting a dual degree: "I was fascinated by the relationship," he told us in a lengthy phone interview. Goldsmith began auditing law school while he was in medical school; after finishing medical school he went ahead and got his law degree. He practices medical-legal law (both defense and plaintiff work) in New York City.

"Having an MD/LLB gives me the best of both worlds," he enthused. "I have to keep up with my medicine, and I have to keep up with my law. And I'm in an area of the law that is constantly breaking new ground: you've got the right-to-die [issue], you've got surrogacy, you have the abortion problem, you have the med-mal problem, you have the health-care quality assurance act. Everything is breaking. If you pick up the *New York Times,* there's an article about health insurance. Not one day goes by without medical-legal implications. The intellectual stimulation is fantastic."

What do MD/JDs do? Many do full-time medical-malpractice work (usually for the defense), Goldsmith said. Others practice law full-time, but not in med-mal. Still others practice medicine full-time and use their law training in their medical practice.

Who do you interact with in the field? If you're practicing medicine, Goldsmith pointed out, you're dealing with physicians, nurses, and patients in a patient setting. "Well, I'm not treating patients, but I'm certainly interacting with patients on a daily basis. We represent and defend the hospital. Physicians call me all the time. I'm interacting, but I'm doing it differently—I'm not treating a patient. I don't have to make this decision. [Instead], I can second-guess everybody."

What are the risks? When Goldsmith first decided to take the plunge, some lawyers tried to discourage him. "They felt that as a physician/lawyer I'd be neither fish nor fowl," he explained. "You're not a physician, you're not an attorney. Well, if you try to do both, you probably can't practice medicine on a regular basis, and practice law on a regular basis, and do either well. Both are too demanding. But if you're going to do it, the opportunity is there for you to take, just like anything else. You might say that in medicine you're more likely to be guaranteed a comfortable living," he pointed out. "In law you're not going to be given that guarantee. You've got to make your own way. And there are a lot of people out there competing with you for the same business."

How is the law different from medicine? One MD/JD, writing in *Medical Economics,*[6] described the difference this way: "Doctors tend to look at the blacks and whites of situations and see specific sets of facts that they use to reach a conclusion. The patient is sick; he exhibits these symptoms; therefore he has either A, B, or C. On the other hand, lawyers see everything in shades of gray. The facts are useful only if they lead to the desired conclusion. There are no wrong or right conclusions in law. What conclusion the lawyer attempts to reach depends on which side he represents."

After getting his law degree, the MD/JD (who was an internist) decided to return to medicine. "Does that mean the outlay was wasted money?" he asked himself. "No. Law school taught me a new way to reason. It helped me organize facts and ideas, and present arguments more convincingly."

Lee Goldsmith called it "speaking two languages." Some MDs have a hard time adjusting to the new thought process; they have difficulty making a legal decision, according to a recruiter within a large law firm. "If you've really been into the practice of medicine you can sometimes analyze the thing to death," said Goldsmith.

Are certain medical specialties more appropriate to the law? "A lot of psychiatrists use the law because they get into forensic psychiatry, and a group of pathologists as well get into forensic pathology. But aside from that there are myriad individuals and situations."

What should I expect from a career of practicing law? "Physicians sometimes have very distorted views of what law is going to be able to do for them," Goldsmith said. "They think that medicine has been so nice and secure, and law is going to be the same thing—'Hey, I've got an MD/JD, I'm going to be at the top of the heap.' It's not that way."

What about that notion that law is less work for more money? "You can still take certain areas of medicine and work nine to five," Goldsmith replied. "You cannot do that in the law. I may not get called at two or three in the morning, and I may not be on call all night, but I'm usually here by 7:30 am and I usually spend my evenings writing."

If Goldsmith were searching for an MD/JD to join his staff, what kind of characteristics would he look for? Who are the folks who'd be most likely to land the job? "Someone who is outgoing, and verbal, and willing to mix and mingle," Goldsmith said. "We're in a business, and we're out there as a business to constantly get business, constantly be known." Quite often someone who has been practicing medicine isn't used to that marketing mentality.

Another requirement for the job is the ability to make a decision and stick with it. Goldsmith explains the situation: "We get 20 potential malpractice cases a week, in which they want to sue physicians. Out of those 20 cases, there is going to be maybe one that we'll accept. There are 10 we should get rid of within 5 minutes over the phone, because they're blatantly not what we want to be involved in."

Why? Because it's not a strong case, it's not up your alley, or what?

"Some of them are just schizophrenic; they want to sue because 'the doctor has implanted an electrode in their brain which is allowing the government to control them,' and so on. You have to get rid of those calls fast," Goldsmith said. "And then there are others who call and say, 'The dentist removed the wrong tooth.' And you get rid of those calls as fast as you can—and the associates have to be able to do it. Then, of the remaining cases, you really have to know where you're going to spend your time and money to evaluate. You've got to be able to hone in.

"Let's say somebody comes in with a situation, but you know it's going to cost $3,000 to $4,000 to get all of the records. Well, are you going to spend the money there, or will you take a deeper medical history and find out what's really going on? You weed out the cases until you have those that you (and everybody else) can look at and say, 'Yes, this is malpractice. This person has been injured and they have a justified situation. This case can be processed easily.'"

So the malpractice law firm only wants to take on cases that have some likelihood of success, because its fees come out of the settlement and not from the clients?

"Most of the malpractice cases that are brought should not be brought," Goldsmith replied. "Seventy percent are dropped without payment of funds." A good law firm, however, will collect money on 95% of its cases, simply because it is more careful about the caliber of the lawsuit.

What else can an MD/JD do? Get involved in medical ethics, for one thing. David Orentlicher, MD, JD, staffed the AMA Council on Ethical and Judicial Affairs. "I'm able to work on interesting issues using both medicine and law," he reports. "The analysis is more of a legal analysis than a medical analysis." People ask Orentlicher if they should get a law degree. "If you want to *use* your law degree, then get it," he advises. "But to get the degree just for the sake of having the credential is a mistake."

Other MD/JDs go into teaching or they work for the government. Wherever law and medicine rub shoulders, there's a spot for an MD/JD. "Every government agency that deals with health issues has a legal office," explained Orentlicher, "and I'm sure the lawyers there feel very uncomfortable when they have to get into technical issues."

What can an MD/JD expect to earn? "There is no range," said Goldsmith, referring to malpractice law. "There's no upper limit; there's no lower limit. You can go bust being an MD/JD and you can make a fortune. It's the capability of the individual." Orentlicher estimated that an MD/JD's earnings in a private law firm would be around $70,000, perhaps less than that for government work. Senior policy positions would pay more.

What sorts of questions should MDs interested in the law ask themselves? "The first thing they should ask themselves is, 'Why am I doing this?'" Goldsmith said. "Because if they're going to spend four years going to school at night and they have two kids at home, do they really want to do that? Is it being fair, or are they trying to escape a situation?"

Goldsmith strongly recommends talking to other MD/JDs. "I would advise a physician who wants to get a law degree to call a half dozen of us, go out of his or her way to meet us, and get a feel as to whether it's something he or she really wants to do. Most of the individuals I know with the MD/JD degree are very accessible. I can't think of anyone who is not."

Is there a particular temperament suited to the law? Jay Gold, MD, JD, is the executive director of the American College of Legal Medicine (see address on next page). He said it's difficult to generalize about temperament, because there's a range of temperaments among both lawyers and doctors. He hypothesized, "Any particular temperament you found in one professional could carry over somewhere in the other one. The litigator who's very aggressive might carry over to the surgeon who's very aggressive. The guy who reads things over and thinks up a new line of attack may have his counterpart in the subspecialist who can come up with the diagnosis that nobody else can."

Gold pointed out that law, more than medicine, is a matter of using words. "Words are very important to medicine, now more than ever, what with the importance of medical records. But the measure of medicine isn't whether you've managed to verbally persuade; it's whether you've managed to cure. And that's completely independent of how good an arguer you are."

Is there room for one more lawyer? "A week doesn't go by that some physician doesn't tell me that he or she has thought about going to law school," Gold told us. "I tell them there's certainly a market for physicians with law degrees who want to practice law."

Resources for information about opportunities for MD/JDs

American College of Legal Medicine
(1,450 members)
611 E Wells St
Milwaukee, WI 53202
414 276-1881; 800 433-9137
Publishes the *Journal of Legal Medicine* (quarterly), the *ACLM Newsletter,*
and *Legal Medicine Perspectives* (quarterly)

American Society of Law, Medicine, and Ethics
(4,200 members)
765 Commonwealth Ave, 16th Floor
Boston, MA 02215
617 262-4990
Publishes *American Journal of Law and Medicine* (quarterly) and the *Journal of Law, Medicine and Ethics* (quarterly)

Other Nonclinical Fields

Teaching

If you're looking for a place where malpractice isn't a factor and where you won't have to deal with the problems doctors routinely face, teaching may be just the thing. And as one physician put it, the government hasn't tried to ruin it (yet).

Medical publishing

The 1995 membership directory of the American Medical Writers Association indicates that 11.5% of its members are MDs or DOs.

American Medical Writers Association
(4,000 members)
9650 Rockville Pike
Bethesda, MD 20814-3998
301 493-0003

Other Associations of Interest

When you contact the associations that may be relevant to your career interest, ask for sample issues of their newsletter or journal. Talk with the executive director to find out what the organization offers someone in your position. Find out if the association conducts salary surveys of its members.

Aerospace Medical Association
(3,600 members)
320 S Henry St
Alexandria, VA 22314-3579
703 739-2240

American College of Occupational and Environmental Medicine
(7,000 members)
55 W Seegers Rd
Arlington Heights, IL 60005
847 228-6850

American Association of Medical Society Executives
(1,200 members)
515 N State St
Chicago, IL 60610
312 464-2555

American College of Medical Quality
(2,000 members)
9005 Congressional Ct
Potomac, MD 20854
301 365-3570

American Academy of Insurance Medicine
(650 members)
9005 Congressional Ct
Potomac, MD 20854
301 365-3572

The Society of Medical Consultants to the Armed Forces
(1,100 members)
USUHS
PO Box 2700
Kensington, MD 20891-2700
301 295-3903

Making Your Own Opportunities

When it comes to finding or creating a satisfying career, the bottom line, of course—for physicians or for anyone—is that it's all up to us: to our creativity, ingenuity, persistence, openness to new ideas and new situations—and our willingness to take well-measured risks. "Some people in medicine are extreme entrepreneurs," Woeppel observed. "They've had some touch of business in some way, shape, or form, apart from just their medical practice. They have a tendency to be always looking for [opportunities]."

Can I Afford to Make the Change?

It's difficult to generalize about the incomes of physicians who change careers. Some experience an increase in income, others a decrease, and for still others their income stays about the same. If there is a decrease, in some cases it's only temporary; the physician quickly climbs the new career ladder—or his or her new consulting business takes off. Others never recapture the high earnings of previous years, but perhaps that's not their most important goal.

How do you find out about the incomes for the field you're interested in? Here are some suggestions:

- *Network, network, network.* Seek out people who are doing what you're thinking about moving into. Develop relationships; ask lots of questions. Although people generally are reluctant to disclose their own salary figures, they may be willing to give you an idea of the range, particularly if you "network back"—that is, share with them what you've learned about their field so far.

- *Contact associations.* Many trade associations conduct salary surveys of their members. Contact the associations that pertain to your field of interest. Don't ignore the nonmedical groups that might be of help; for example, a physician interested in writing should contact local publishing groups in addition to the American Medical Writers Association.

- *Read the classified ads.* Follow the trade journals for your field, keeping in mind that the benefits that add substantially to a compensation package are frequently negotiable and infrequently advertised.

- *Talk to physician recruiters and executive recruiters.* They're in the business of knowing who's doing what and who's getting what. Whether you're changing specialties, changing geographic areas, or changing positions, they'll have the best sense of what you can *realistically* expect.

Notes to Part 2

1. Schwartz H. Seeking greener pastures: many doctors are entering other professions. *Private Practice*. March 1985;17:42.

2. Rucker TD, Keller MD, eds. *Careers in Medicine: Traditional and Alternative Opportunities*. Garrett Park, Md: Garrett Park Press; 1986:223-245. Also see 1990 edition.

3. Bluestein P. Physicians in transition. *Physician Executive*. December 1995:16.

4. Reuters. Doctors seek MBAs to handle health market changes. *Reuters Asia/Pacific Business Report*. May 25, 1995.

5. Bluestein, 19.

6. Morisaki M. How I learned not to be a lawyer. *Medical Economics*. June 11, 1984:167-169.

Part 3
Taking the Next Step

What's Your Pitch?

Before you embark on your actual job search for a nonclinical position, it's important to be clear about how you're going to present yourself—not only to prospective employers and executive recruiters, but also to the many people you'll be networking with. (If you work with a career consultant, he or she can help you with this, perhaps by using mock interviews on videotape.) If you present yourself clearly to people in your network, chances are good that they'll represent you clearly when they pass on word of you through the network to others. Prepare them adequately! If you want people to communicate to others that you're upbeat and enthusiastic about your new career possibilities, demonstrate that in your conversations with them. They can't manufacture it on their own.

As we discussed in part 1, many people (physicians and nonphysicians alike) see being a physician as the ultimate job, and they will not understand why you would want to do something else. In fact, some will be downright suspicious. Be positive—and focus on the future. If it's relevant, explain to people the ways in which what you're planning to do builds on or is an extension of what you were doing in the past. Play up the work experience that's applicable to what you now want to do, and play down what's not.

Who Are You?

If a hiring organization's recruitment team has done their work, they will have a sense of the ideal personal qualifications for the job. You can help the process move along if you know whether your ideals—and theirs—match.

- How would you characterize yourself?

_____

_____

_____

_____

_____

- How would you describe your personality, values, and character?

_____

_____

_____

_____

_____

- How do you get along with others?

  _____

  _____

  _____

  _____

  _____

- How do you cope with change? Do you run from it or thrive on it?

  _____

  _____

  _____

  _____

  _____

- What's your management style?

  _____

  _____

  _____

  _____

  _____

Some organizations are looking for a team-builder; others want a bottom-line manager. Do you have management expertise? Is smoothing ruffled feathers and resolving conflicts your special skill? Are you good at making decisions? How are your practice-management skills; did you like managing your own practice, or was that the least desirable aspect of being in practice?

If you feel reticent about discussing such things—particularly your view of yourself—this area may take some work. It's worth the effort, however, because interviewers *will* ask such questions. They're not just interested in your clinical abilities and the content of your answers; they'll be trying to evaluate how much insight you have into yourself, how articulate you are, and how well you'll mesh with the team.

Job Searching as Relationship Building

Although the authors of *Physician Recruitment and Retention: Practical Techniques for Exceptional Results* speak from the perspective of physician recruiters, not candidates, from either side of the coin, the principles are the same. "Recruitment of high-level professionals in all industries has always been based on relationship building," Roger G. Bonds and Kimberly A. Pulliam write. "Building the relationship simply means getting to know one another and developing trust. This takes time. The process of building relationships…can take several months, and some relationships may take two or more years to solidify."[1]

The candidate would be wise to look at every contact with a search consultant or a prospective employer as an opportunity to build on that relationship and trust. As Bonds and Pulliam explain, the "magnitude of such a decision is so great that all parties should be confident that they can trust each other and understand each other's needs, expectations, and philosophies. [Deciding on a career path] is a major life and business decision."[2]

Whose Job Is It to Find You a Job?

Who should you rely on the most when looking for a job? Even the search consultants we talked to suggested that the place to start was with your own network. Physician recruiters can be an important part of your network—but they shouldn't be the whole thing. Don't expect to hand search consultants a wish list of what you want and then sit back and wait for them to find it. Search consultants can augment your search efforts, not replace them. (Conversely, don't exclude search consultants from your network; they can offer valuable advice, information, and contacts.) So get on the phone, call your contacts, and call the people *they* suggest you call—you'll soon be well on your way.

The Value of Networking

Someone once said that each person in the United States—no matter who he or she may be—is only five phone calls away from the President. That is, we each know someone we could call, who knows someone else they could call, who knows someone, who knows someone, who could call the Oval Office. Keep that in mind in all your networking relationships. Every person you meet has the potential to help you achieve your career goals—either directly, themselves, or by making a few phone calls on your behalf. They may be in a position to hire you (or buy the product you're selling, etc) or they may know somebody, who knows somebody, who knows somebody else…who may be in a position to hire you—or at least to help you in some way. Whichever camp people are in, they deserve your attention. Although looking at life this way may seem self-serving, it's not, really; it's simply pragmatic, another way of recognizing the interdependency of us all.

How to Expand Your Network

Start by thinking about what you're willing and able to *give*, not looking to get (although that's legitimate, too). Commit yourself to being responsive to others' inquiries and needs. Think about what you are and are not willing to give, and out of that will come an ease in asking others for assistance. People really are willing to help; it's simply a matter of building relationships. Build a reputation as someone who's helpful and others will be eager to help you.

Get your materials ready

Have a supply of business cards always on your person and a supply of thank-you notes and stamps always on your desk. Get a larger-size card-file system, if necessary, to accommodate the extra names you'll be adding to your system.

Acknowledge people's help

Within a day or two of receiving someone's help, drop a note in the mail. It doesn't need to be long or gushy; it can simply say, "I appreciate the time you took." Business-stationery stores, including some mail-order firms, now offer a variety of note cards to suit any professional's needs.

Set up your notation system

At the very least, make a mental note to be responsive to the person who helped you when and if he or she ever asks you for help (in the next month, next year, or next decade). Better yet, add the helper's card to your card file with a notation of when and how he or she helped you. Then the helper's name is handy in case you need help again—or in case others need help. Sales professionals routinely jot down every contact with a client, and that's a good networking strategy, too. Whenever you talk to someone in your network, make a note of it: "Recommended that I call Dr Miller…" "Promised to send me salary survey by end of month…" "Sent her a copy of my CV [date]." "Used to work with Dr Karkkainen at XYZ Pharmaceuticals…" While you're building your own personal network, you'll be creating a system for others to selectively tap into—just as they've allowed you to tap into theirs.

Accept a "no" gracefully

Remember, no one's obliged to talk to you, and there will be those who seemingly can't be bothered or who aren't responsive—in other words, they haven't yet discovered the value of networking. Others may genuinely want to help, but they simply don't have the information you need. In any case, be gracious.

Define what's confidential and what's not

If you're thinking about leaving your present position but don't want that information broadcast around the country just yet, clearly spell that out for the people you're networking with. Don't assume they'll automatically know what should remain private and what shouldn't; let them know clearly what they may and may not share. And ask the same of them when you're listening to them talk about their situation: Is it OK to share this information with others? Obviously, respecting these boundaries is essential; networking is all about building relationships and building trust, and the trust will be destroyed if we misuse the information others give us.

Defining Your Ideal Job: A Questionnaire

According to Bonds and Pulliam, health-care organizations are working harder to recruit, launching aggressive campaigns. Recruitment has become a high priority because health-care organizations need physicians "to stay in business and provide high-quality care to the community."[3] Ideally, an organization's recruiting is "based on a manpower plan, a systematic analysis of the number and types of physicians the organization needs to recruit."[4] The recruiters in the organization know what the organization needs.

Remember, recruiting is selling. Recruiters are well-versed salespeople, trying to persuade you that their opportunity is the one for you. You should be equally well-versed in what you want and need—in both your professional and personal lives. By answering these questions (either by yourself or, preferably, with your family), you'll better clarify your target job. While answering each of the questions, also ask yourself: What's my bottom line in this area? Is what I've defined here necessary (and thus nonnegotiable)? Is it preferred (but negotiable)? Or is it unacceptable (and nonnegotiable)?

- How many hours a week do I want to work?

_____

_____

- How many hours a week do I want to spend on patient care?

_____

_____

- What's the ideal balance for me between clinical and nonclinical work?

  _____

  _____

  _____

- Which kinds of patient-care activities am I interested in? Which am I _not_ interested in?

  _____

  _____

  _____

  _____

- What kind of nonclinical work do I want to do? (Administrator, teacher, medical director, researcher, marketing director, writer...)

  _____

  _____

  _____

  _____

- In which field do I want to work? (Pharmaceuticals, hospital administration, managed care, education, public relations, publishing, association management, medical computing, legal medicine...)

  _____

  _____

  _____

  _____

- What would be the principal focus of my work? (Managing the employee health program, assuring the quality of treatment, conducting research on AIDS...)

  _____

  _____

  _____

  _____

- In my ideal job, what tasks would I be performing? What tasks would I *not* be performing?

  _____

  _____

  _____

  _____

- What type of organization do I prefer? (For instance, hospital, the military, HMO, medical association, pharmaceutical manufacturing firm, advertising agency, research laboratory, etc)

  _____

  _____

  _____

- What size organization would I want to work in?

  _____

  _____

  _____

- What is my preferred organization's position within its marketplace, including its revenues, number of employees, image, and range of products and services?

  _____

  _____

  _____

  _____

- What kinds of reporting relationships suit me best? Where do I want to sit on the organizational chart? Do I want to work alone? Be in charge of a team, reporting directly to the CEO? Or do I want to be the CEO?

  _____

  _____

  _____

  _____

- How important is autonomy (ease of decision making) to me? How much bureaucracy can I tolerate?

  _____

  _____

  _____

- How much responsibility do I want to have for supervising/managing others?

  _____

  _____

  _____

- In my ideal job, how much would I interact with other MDs?

  _____

  _____

  _____

- What is my preferred work schedule? How predictable is it? Do I require weekends off? Would I be interested in a job that routinely requires me to be away from home in the evenings? Am I looking for nine to five?

  _____

  _____

  _____

- In my ideal work environment, what's the usual pace of the office?

  _____

  _____

  _____

- What are my financial goals? How much do I want to be making a year from now? Five years from now? What kind of compensation package am I looking for?

  _____

  _____

  _____

- Do I have sufficient resources to make this change? Have I set aside enough funds to cover transition costs?

  _____

  _____

  _____

- How would I define the ideal lifestyle for me and my family? (Quality of schools, time for leisure activities, cultural opportunities, proximity to major university, etc) (*Don't overlook these important considerations. In recruiters' experience, community and lifestyle count the most to physicians. In fact, recruiters claim there's a "40-60 rule"—professional aspects count 40% in the physician's decision, and personal aspects 60%.*[5])

  _____

  _____

  _____

  _____

- Which geographical area do I prefer? (West Coast, Midwest, Southwest, etc)

  _____

  _____

- Are my family and I willing to relocate?

  _____

  _____

- What kind of community do I want to work in? Live in? (Large city, suburban, medium-size city, small town/rural)

  _____

  _____

  _____

- What kind of neighborhood is right for me and my family? (Friendliness, crime rate, population density, type of housing, access to schools and public transportation, availability of leisure and social activities, etc)

_____

_____

_____

_____

What Are You Selling? To Whom?

Your job search will be more effective if you understand it as a sales situation. It's important to be clear about what you are selling (what do you have to offer?) and who you are selling it to (what are the organization's needs?).

As you prepare your marketing plan, think in terms of the concrete benefits you can bring to a prospective employer. What problems can you solve for the organization, and how will the organization benefit from your work?

Hospitals are used to looking at physicians in terms of what they bring in and what they cost. Bonds and Pulliam write, "A 1990 study by Jackson and Coker and Ernst & Young suggests that each physician generates an average of $678,000 per year in inpatient and outpatient revenue."[6]

Crafting an Effective CV*

Fair or not, we live in a world of snap judgments. This is especially true where careers are concerned. No matter what position you're seeking, chances are that you will be only one of many candidates to be screened by the person or committee that can bring you into the organization. And when these people are confronted by many applicants at once, the time they are likely to spend reviewing any one curriculum vitae (CV) can be counted in seconds, not minutes. That's why your CV can be so important. A good CV alone will not guarantee the position you want. But a bad CV can shut the door on you before you get a chance to discuss your qualifications.

From an executive recruiter's perspective, the CV is a tool for identifying candidates whose backgrounds best match the job. It tells them who you are and what you've done, and suggests what you may bring to the organization. The interviewer can also use it as a guide for asking questions that will help him or her assess how useful your skills and experiences will be to the position. In supplying that needed information, your job in writing a CV is to summarize your

* "Crafting an Effective CV" was written by Joe Ann Jackson. Adapted from the version published in _American Medical News,_ August 19, 1991.

employment history, education, training, and credentials. It's also the opportunity to list your major accomplishments, such as published articles and awards.

Over the years we have reviewed thousands of physician CVs. Mixed in with the ones that were well prepared and printed on high-quality paper were some typed on notebook paper and a few that were even written on prescription pads. We have seen CVs that were half-typed and half-handwritten. Quite a few had been photocopied so many times that the type was not clearly readable. And a number of them contained misspelled medical terms. It's obvious that quite a few physicians haven't gotten the message about preparing an effective CV. With that in mind, here are some CV basics:

CVs generally fall into two formats, *chronological* and *functional.* Chronological CVs arrange your work experiences, training, and education sequentially, beginning with the present and working back in time. Functional CVs provide you with a format to outline your accomplishments. A functional CV is especially useful in highlighting an important phase of your career and training.

Which format is best for you? There is no pat answer, but physicians, perhaps more than job seekers in other professions, have a greater stake in emphasizing training and clinical knowledge. For that reason, many may prefer the functional-format CV. Rather than just listing a chronological account of your training and the jobs you have held, it focuses on the sum of your experience and skills gathered under many circumstances.

On the other hand, a chronological CV is often shorter, and that allows a prospective employer to quickly skim it for key credentials. It also takes less time to prepare.

Regardless of which format you choose, it is extremely important to tailor your CV to the type of position and organization you are looking for. This doesn't mean that you should prepare a customized CV for each job you apply for. But it helps to include information that shows that your experience and credentials are a strong fit for the job you are looking to move to. For example, you may have administrative, managerial, or writing skills that set you apart from other candidates. On another tack, you may have experience with a medical procedure that requires a high competence level and gives you a competitive edge. The key is that your clinical expertise may be of little interest to an employer looking primarily for an administrator. Likewise, a group looking for someone to be primarily a clinician may not be intrigued by a CV geared to an administrative slot.

For that reason, the more you know about the type of position you are looking for, the better. Know the approximate size of the facility, the number of physicians (or physician executives, or pharmaceutical researchers, and so on) on staff, and the nature of the work you'd be doing. This will give you ideas about what to include in your CV.

One of the best ways to custom-tailor a CV to a specific position is with a cover letter. By adding relevant information not shown in the CV, you can bridge the gap between the experience listed on the CV and the specific requirements of the job. More than that, a personal letter is a positive expression of interest in the job that will probably be well received by the person reading it.

The cover letter should not summarize your CV nor be longer than a single page. Length is also a key consideration in preparing a CV. We recommend that your CV not exceed three pages; many recruiters say that they do not have the time to read more than that.

Given these constraints, you should think carefully about what you want to put in your CV and how you want to represent your qualifications. If you have published articles, you may want to cite those that are relevant to the position. You should not, however, submit copies of the articles or write extensive summaries—they just add bulk to the CV. And photos are not necessary.

What information should you leave out of your CV? *Don't include:*

- Race

- Religion

- Anticipated compensation

- Reasons for leaving previous positions

- Health problems or disabilities

- Examination scores

- Medical license numbers

- DEA number

You may also eliminate references to:

- Age
- Place of birth
- Citizenship
- Marital status

Your CV should be printed on high-quality paper—either white or light beige. The typefaces used are important to the appearance of the CV. With many styles and sizes on the market, you have a variety from which to choose. However, you should limit the number of typefaces to two or three.

Practically nothing undercuts the credibility of a CV more than misspellings or typos. Have someone knowledgeable proofread your CV carefully, especially for medical terms. If all this sounds like too much work, there are résumé firms that will custom prepare your CV based on the information you provide; they can even typeset it for a more polished look. When considering such firms, ask if they are experienced with physician CVs, which use a different format than other types of professional résumés.

Whether your CV is professionally prepared or written on your own, remember that there is no one perfect CV format nor any CV that will be liked by everyone who reads it. But every bit of effort that goes into a CV shows, and a well-prepared CV can set you apart from the competition.

Chronological CV—Sample Outline

- Name
- Address—home and office/hospital
- Telephone—home and office/hospital
- Certification and licensure—for example, "Board Certified in Internal Medicine, September 1988," or "Diplomate, National Board of Medical Examiners, July 1995"
- Education—list in descending order, with most recent listed first, noting name of college/university, degree received, and dates
- Postgraduate training—list all training, such as internship, residency, fellowships, and so on, with name of institution and dates
- Work experience (including practicing medicine)—list in descending order, with most recent listed first

- Professorial or teaching appointments
- Awards and honors
- Professional society memberships
- Languages spoken
- Personal and professional references—"Furnished on request"
- Bibliography—presentations, publications

Painting Mental Pictures

Whichever CV format you use, don't settle for just a list of job titles. Use action words (*increased, overhauled, directed, negotiated, secured, designed, implemented,* and so on) that build a mental picture of what you actually accomplished, and that show how you were a star. Add statistics wherever possible to bolster your assertion; for example, "Reduced annual staff turnover by 24%," "Increased patient visits by 15% over 6 months," "Co-taught leadership seminar to 10 senior administrators," or "Revamped group-practice accounting system." These words not only allow the reader to picture you in action, but they also demonstrate that you're someone who is used to measuring your success in concrete terms.

Your community service and involvement in civic affairs may be relevant, particularly if your change of work environment is striking (say, from a family practitioner in a small group to an executive in a Fortune 100 corporation). Potential employers, consciously or not, will be wondering whether you'll fit into the new work culture.

The trick is to think about the skills needed in your target position and to highlight those skills on your CV—build a bridge, in other words, between you and the position. Perhaps as a physician in solo practice you haven't had a lot of managerial experience. But perhaps as a parent volunteer you headed up the annual fund-raising campaign for your children's school (and managed a corps of 50 other volunteers); that information is definitely relevant to your CV.

Some professionals use two CVs: a short, one- or two-pager that describes the essential elements of their training, experience, and capabilities; and a longer version that elaborates on those points and includes an extensive bibliography, and so on. The professionals offer the shorter CV at the time of the initial inquiry and provide the longer CV at (or just before) the personal interview.

Regardless of whether you actually distribute a longer-version CV, writing one (carefully detailing all your accomplishments and thinking hard about how you want to describe them) can be a useful exercise. In any case, you need to have thought all that through so you can be articulate when talking to recruiters or potential employers about your accomplishments.

When to Update Your CV

Even if you're not actively looking for a new position, you should keep your CV up-to-date. Since life has a way of taking unexpected turns, it's better to be prepared. Take out your CV and reread it at least once or twice a year. (You may be surprised at how quickly things change.) As a document, your CV should steadily evolve just as your career does. Even if you haven't changed jobs since the last update, you may want to make subtle but important changes—in the way you describe what you do, in the order in which you present things, or in the emphasis you put on particular items.

Update the CV whenever you develop new skills, receive an award, publish additional articles or books, join another professional organization, or receive additional training. The best way to accomplish this is to keep your CV on your computer, where you can update and change it at will.

However you produce your CV, have it proofread by one or more publishing professionals!

Preparing Your References

Contact the people you'd like to use as references to get their permission and—equally important—their support and cooperation in your job search. Talk through with them what you're looking for, so they can be articulate and enthusiastic about you when a hiring organization contacts them. Ideally, they'll hear your enthusiasm for the move and they'll communicate that to the organization calling. Prepare them!

If you don't prepare your references, you may run the risk of your target organization hearing something like this: "You're asking me about Dr H? Last I heard from her was 1962…"

To protect your references from being inconvenienced by too many unsolicited calls, simply state on your CV that references "will be furnished on request." You would want to evaluate a job opportunity, anyway, before you release the names of your references.

Some organizations ask for three personal references and three professional ones—and then go even further, by asking each reference, "Do you know anyone else who's familiar with Dr Z's work?" And then the recruiter will call those names. If it feels appropriate, you may want to discuss with your references the answers they plan to give to that question.

We should note that the search consultants we spoke with all said that "going three deep" isn't routinely done. As Randy Gott, the Director of Development at Jackson and Coker, said, "We go as deep as the doctor will allow us to go. What we mean by that is if [a candidate] says to me, 'Randy, I'll give you these three references,' [then] those are the three we call. And the reason is because we don't want to do *anything* that will jeopardize his particular position. And when you start, in my opinion, going that second or third or fourth level, you're going beyond what he's given you permission to do."

Beginning Your Search

- Identify the professional skills needed in your new field of interest. If you don't have them, consider taking courses to acquire them. This will make you more marketable.

- Learn to use a personal computer; it may be helpful in your next position.

- The classified job ads in publications relevant to your target field are a first stop, of course. But even beyond offering ads, the publications can give you an idea of the key people in the field, particularly if the field is new to you. If you're looking for a position as a medical director, you'd want to follow the classified ads in the *Journal of the American Medical Association* and the *New England Journal of Medicine.*

- Contact key industry leaders.

- Use your contacts at professional associations, such as the American College of Physician Executives and your citywide and statewide medical societies.

- If your target work setting is a hospital, contact local hospital councils or state hospital associations.

- Register with the placement services sponsored by medical associations.

- Use your computer not only to compose and keep track of your career-related correspondence, but also as a source of information about jobs; see "Using the Internet as a Career Resource," next page.

- Contact physician recruiters (in-house recruitment departments and search firms).

- Contact your medical school. Its placement office may be of help, even if you graduated some years ago. The placement or alumnus affairs office may receive inquiries from potential employers, and they may be able to put you in touch with other alums who could be of help in your search.

- Submit reports to journals, magazines, or local newspapers, as a contributing writer, on studies you have completed. This will help to get your name out.

- Increase your visibility. Volunteer to work on a research project in a field or area of your interest.

- Contact your medical school deans, associate deans, department chairpeople, and professors.

- Contact the instructors of the continuing education courses you've taken.

- Attend conferences in your new field of interest; this is an excellent way to learn more about a profession and meet new people who may be able to help you.

- *Most of all, talk to physicians who are doing what you want to do.*

Some last suggestions in this vein: conducting a job search takes considerable time and effort. Put job-seeking activities on your calendar; set aside specific times to implement your career-change plan. And be in touch with your lawyer. Let him or her know you're planning a job change and you'd like some help drafting letters of agreement, negotiating your compensation package, and/or reviewing the final employment contract.

Using the Internet as a Career Resource

The Internet is a global network of computer networks, linking millions of computers and over 25 million computer users. The Internet provides numerous resources for physicians, including many job searching facilities set up specifically for them as a group.

To get access to the Internet, you need a computer, a modem, special software, and an account with a major online service (such as CompuServe or America Online) or with a local Internet service provider. There are dozens of books available that will help explain how to get connected. *Physicians' Guide to the Internet* by Lee Hancock (Lippincott-Raven, 1996) includes an introduction on how to get connected to the Internet and a healthy listing of Internet resources devoted to medicine. *The Lawyer's Guide to the Internet* by G. Burgess Allison (American Bar Association, 1995) was written with professionals in mind and provides a cogent, concise, and witty introduction to the Internet.

The Internet provides several services, including electronic mail, file transfer, remote access, and information "browsing" using the World Wide Web. The

World Wide Web (or WWW or the Web for short) is a system of linked documents stored on computers that are "viewed" by means of browser software. (Mosaic and Netscape are two common graphical browsers.) Web documents can include text, pictures, sound, and even short video segments. Web documents or sites (collections of documents) have "addresses" called URLs (Uniform Resource Locators); these have the prefix "http://" and are typed into the software to access the document. The following are just a few of the career resources for physicians available on the World Wide Web:

American College of Physician Executives (http://www.acpe.org/home.html)

The ACPE's web site contains information about this organization as well as listings of educational seminars, events, and publications. Most valuable for career changers, however, is the career opportunities page, which contains listings of job openings for physician executives.

MedSearch America (http://www.medsearch.com)

MedSearch America is a service for both physicians and employers seeking physicians. Physicians and other medical personnel can upload their résumés to a database, which can be searched by employers. Also, employers can post job openings, which can be searched by physicians. The service is free to physicians, but available for a charge to employers.

MedConnect (http://www.medconnect.com)

MedConnect offers a variety of medical news and information as well as an interactive jobs list. An interactive education area offers CME credit for viewing the material and taking an interactive quiz. The site also has interactive forums, information on new products, "cases of the month," and an Internet tutorial.

Physician's Guide to the Internet (http://www.webcom.com/pgi/welcome.html)

This site is designed for physicians "who want to take advantage of the many and rapidly changing information resources on the Internet." The following resources are available here: Physician Lifestyle, Clinical Practice, Postgraduate Education, FunStuff, New Physician, Today's News, Medical Puzzlers, Medical Newsbits, PGI's Job Board, and Products and Services for Physicians.

Physicians Employment (http://www.fairfield.com/physemp/index.html)

This service offers job opportunities for physicians, allied health and nursing openings, a list of fellowship programs, and a directory of physician recruitment firms.

PracticeLink (http://www.practicelink.com/)

This site lists hospitals and medical groups that are actively recruiting physicians. PracticeLink offers a free copy of their "White Pages," a telephone directory of hospitals and medical groups (and their key medical staff personnel) currently involved in physician recruiting.

American Medical Association (http://www.ama-assn.org)

The AMA's award-winning web site holds the current physician recruitment advertising ads from *JAMA*. You can also access the current text of all AMA journals and get more information about AMA books on practice management and managed care.

How to Work Effectively With Search Consultants

To gather information for this section, we contacted two search firms: Jackson and Coker, a physician-recruitment firm in Atlanta, and Kieffer, Ford and Hadelman, a health-care-executive recruitment firm in Oak Brook, Illinois. Consultants at both firms were kind enough to grant us lengthy phone interviews.

Kieffer, Ford and Hadelman places health-care executives (who may or may not be MDs); they do not recruit for practicing-physician positions. In contrast, more than 99% of the positions for which Jackson and Coker recruits are for practicing physicians. The advice the consultants shared, however, should be relevant to physicians seeking either clinical or nonclinical positions.

The recruiting process consists of identifying and screening candidates, conducting on-site interviews, and successfully negotiating arrangements with finalists. Let's look at the process from the candidate's point of view, and imagine what sorts of questions he or she might have.

Are search firms all alike?

No. Different firms deal with different industries, different positions, and different salary ranges within those industries. You need to find the firms that recruit for your target market. One search consultant recommended checking out the back of *Modern Healthcare,* which lists openings in hospitals around the country—and, if there's a search firm involved, who the search firm is. If you're interested in an administrative position and want to find out which search firms service that area, you could also talk to the hospital administrators you know. Get recommendations from them. For a list of physician-recruitment firms, contact:

National Association of Physician Recruiters
222 S Westmonte Dr, Suite 101
PO Box 150127
Altamonte Springs, FL 32715-0127
407 774-7880

What's the difference between a retained firm and a contingency firm?

Retained search firms are hired by an organization to conduct a search on an exclusive basis. The organization pays a fee (typically a third of the first year's compensation) to conduct the search until the right person is found. A contingency firm, on the other hand, gets paid only if one of the candidates it recommends is hired and performs in the position for an agreed-upon period. In addition, a contingency firm often works on a nonexclusive basis with no guarantee. Because of their more aggressive approach, recruiters from contingency firms are often called "headhunters."

Search consultants who work at retained firms define themselves as management consultants to the client organization. Search consultants say they get fully involved in the organization's needs and are not one-shot headhunters.

What are the limits of the search consultant's role?

Candidates shouldn't confuse a search consultant with a career counselor; while the latter works for you, the former works for the hiring institution. A search consultant is hired by an institution to fill a job, not to help people find jobs. As Mike Doody, a partner at Kieffer, Ford and Hadelman, explained, "We spend a lot of time, however, in career counseling with people, because we're a source that a lot of people go to, seeking out answers. But I think they ought to understand that a search consultant is not in the business of trying to find jobs for people."

Search consultants sometimes walk a fine line, though, in working with clients and candidates. Randy Gott, of Jackson and Coker, explained, "Yes, our client is the hospital, or the HMO, or the group practice—whoever the hiring person is. They're the people who pay us—and we represent them… But we certainly have to work with the candidates, and be an advocate for their candidacy in the eyes of the hiring institutions."

"I'm a practicing physician who's thinking about getting out of practice and moving into administration a year or two down the line, because I'd like to exercise my management and leadership skills more. Where do I start?"

Doody offered this advice: "I think if their interest is moving into a medical administrative position, they should attempt to broaden their exposure as much as possible within the institution where they're practicing medicine, maybe by serving on medical-staff leadership committees and on committees within the hospital, so that they begin to develop a broader perspective and understanding of what makes the organization tick, how it works."

Doody continued, "The typical physician went to undergraduate school (perhaps in pre-med or biology), went on to medical school, and did a residency, maybe a fellowship, and never took organizational courses, management courses, finance courses, marketing courses, and so on. So if he or she could get some exposure to those kinds of disciplines and subject matter, it obviously would be helpful."

"Does my age matter? Will I run into age discrimination if I'm, say, in my 60s?"

According to Mike Doody, rather than age per se, the issue is more the needs of the organization and its mix of people. "Invariably, clients say to us, 'It's what the person brings to us by way of experience, attitude, and energy [that counts],'" he said. "A lot of clients will say, 'Look, I don't want someone who's going to coast downhill on this job. But if the person only wants to give me 5 years, as long as it's 5 hard-driving years, that's fine. I don't need somebody who's going to be here for 20 years.' In fact, a lot of organizations may not want somebody who plans to be there for 20 years—it's not the way a lot of organizations think today. You see a lot of CEOs who are 35 years old, and even though they could be around for another 25 years, they're not necessarily thinking that they're going to be. So it's more a matter of the experience, attitude, style, approach, and level of enthusiasm, than it is [the candidate's] chronological age."

"If I have something in my background that I'm leery of sharing with people—for example, perhaps I was dismissed from my last position—is it OK to stretch the truth a little?"

All the consultants were adamant in their advice to candidates: do *not* lie. Your relationship with the search consultant will probably be seriously damaged, if not destroyed altogether.

What are the repercussions of withholding information? Gott said, "People will wonder what else you've withheld." Doody's response was straightforward: "If I find anybody is lying to me in a résumé, then the conversation ends." Gott added this point: "You must realize that when you use a search firm—as, I would say, when you use your own network and find a job—the firm is almost like an agent for you. It's important that they know the good and the bad. In fact, I would say if a physician contacts Jackson and Coker and there is a problem in his background, the worst thing he can do is not mention it. Because if someone has a problem, a problem is much better dealt with up front than it is after the fact, when people are down the road in terms of interviewing and considering particular candidates."

"Is the old adage true, that it's better to look for a job while you've still got a job?"

"We look at every candidate," Gott replied. "We give them all the benefit of the doubt—until it's proven otherwise. If a physician has been terminated from a practice and is now unemployed, you know that raises a concern, as it would if it was just an employee of a company. If a physician has decided to leave a practice and is looking for a job, we look at that a little bit differently. I guess it all depends on what the situation is… And of course you have to realize there are two sides to every story."

"How do I attract the attention of a search firm? How do I make myself visible?"

The best way is to contact the search firm directly; they usually won't come to you. "Probably one of the best ways for physicians to find a particular job is through their own network," said Gott. "And contacting a recruiting firm basically broadens their horizons, makes them aware of opportunities that they may not be aware of—and may never be aware of—through their own network.

"For example, when a family physician contacts us, all of a sudden he has broadened his horizon by probably 150 opportunities, because we have that many openings right now for family physicians. It's a matter [for us] of talking to that physician and going through a weeding-out process to come up with some [opportunities] that we feel might satisfy his particular needs."

"Besides considering me as a candidate, what can the search firm do for me?"

"Through our discussions with [candidates]," said Gott, "we can make them realize whether what they are looking for is realistic or unrealistic. Everybody wants to live in a city of 2 million people with all the cultural amenities and professional sports—and be on the coast. Well, that may not be realistic." A search firm performs the same reality check for its clients, explained Gott. The firm evaluates whether it is "realistic that this particular institution can attract the kinds of candidates they want."

What is a search consultant looking for in a candidate?

Gott said, "Most of the time our initial contact after we read their inquiry is by phone. [We're looking at] their willingness to cooperate and their willingness to share with us their particular situation, both generally and very specifically."

How thoroughly do search firms check references?

Randy Gott responded this way: "We have the same concern in dealing with a candidate that our clients do, which is that we want to make sure that we are representing a candidate who doesn't have any particular problems that are going to affect his or her particular candidacy. And so, checking out the physician's credentials is a very important part of the whole process, and something that we take very seriously. [However], we cannot jeopardize the physician's present situation in our reference-checking process. That's the 'kiss of death' for the physician's particular practice and in his or her relationship to the medical community... But certainly," Gott continued, "before the physician relocates, the hospital through its credentialing program will definitely have checked out the physician to make sure he or she is everything that it is expecting him or her to be."

Doody responded similarly: "We verify all educational degrees and any certifications or specialties that relate to or are necessary for the position the person is being hired for."

"Will the search firm keep my inquiry confidential?"

"When a physician sends us a CV, we don't send that CV to just anybody," said Gott. "We'll only send that out when we have told the physician that we are going to do that. The physician's CV is not going to get spread all over the country from coast to coast. That's the worst thing that can happen."

"Does the recruiter negotiate my compensation package with me? How soon should I bring up money?"

Typically the search consultant will handle the negotiations. As a candidate bringing up the subject of compensation, though, your timing is important.

As Gott explained: "I would say to a candidate, 'Regardless of the job you're looking for, you need to know what the compensation is before you really ever pursue it to any great degree.' It's a fair question to ask, 'What kind of compensation are you offering?' [But] I don't think it needs to be the first question out of your mouth when you call about a particular job," Gott said. "[If you mention it right away], you may send the wrong message. But it's a given: people expect to be asked that. Through our consultation with them, candidates are aware of *what is reasonable.*"

Michael Doody explained, "If somebody says to me, 'Well, I could be interested, but I want you to know up front that, for various reasons, I would not countenance a move for less than $200,000,' that's legit—that doesn't turn me off. I'd know I was just talking to the wrong guy. But if he said, 'What's it paying?' then I'd really have to wonder…"

Gott cautioned, "[Income] becomes an issue when a guy who has been in practice for 10 years is looking to relocate. He's used to a certain lifestyle and a certain income. It may not be that easy for him to get that same income somewhere else by relocating."

"How quickly will the search consultant respond to me?"

The good ones, from what we can tell, respond quickly to inquiries. Recruiters who have their act together move fast, responding even within a day or two to your phone call or curriculum vitae if you seem to be a likely candidate. Keep in mind, though, that a search consultant's work involves a lot of travel, so if you don't hear anything right away it may be because he or she is out of town.

"How long will it take for me to find my new position?"

"If you're real good, the search can take a month," Doody said. "If you're not so good, it can take forever. That's an impossible question to answer. I think the person has to be prepared for the fact, given today's economy, that it's going to take a long time. And what's a long time? I mean, it could be several months; it could be a couple of years.

"The sooner they start networking with executive search consultants, with their peers, and with their network," Doody added, "the sooner they're going to find potential opportunities, but that doesn't necessarily mean that if you start networking today that next month you're going to have a host of opportunities. It could take a long time, depending on how effective your network is, and what kinds of skills, strengths, talents you bring to the table beyond your medical expertise.

"It will also depend," he said, "on how open you are geographically, and what kind of organization you want to work for. Candidates have to think about all that and make those kinds of decisions."

It's not an overnight process, Doody explained. "Obviously, the more realistic the individual is about his or her strengths, talents, preferences, likes and dislikes, abilities—and the better he or she has zeroed in on the types of positions and organizations that would best match those likes, dislikes, strengths, etc—then the quicker potential that individual has for bringing the search to a successful conclusion more quickly."

"If I know what I'm looking for, should I put that in my cover letter to the recruitment firm?"

"Oh, sure," said Doody. "Because it doesn't do me any good if I've had a telephone conversation with you or gotten material from you indicating your interest in moving into an administrative position, [but] you don't tell me, 'However, I'm only interested in a position in New England.' Chances are the first call I'm going to make to you is going to be about something in Atlanta. Then you'll say, 'Well, I don't want anything in Atlanta, I want New England.'"

"It may not hurt [to spell things out in your cover letter]," said Gott, "but I would also say that a good recruiter will explore those options with the candidate on the phone—it doesn't matter what the cover letter says."

"What can I as a candidate reasonably expect from a search consultant?"

"I think they can expect that when they contact a recruiting firm, that recruiting firm is dead serious about filling the particular position they're calling about," said Gott. Plus, you can expect the search firm to share with you full information about the available position. The firm should be able to tell you the hiring organization's name and location, along with the compensation for the position.

"As many details as they can possibly give you, they should be able to give you," continued Gott. "And if they're unwilling to do that, then I guess I would have to raise my eyebrows. If they're *unable* [to give the information because they don't yet have it], that's another issue." The firm should be willing to find out whatever you need to know, he said. A candidate might ask, for example, "How many emergency-room visits did that hospital have last year?" The consultant's response should be something like this, according to Gott: "I don't know the answer to that, but I can make a quick call and find out for you."

"We tend to be open and direct," Mike Doody said. "We say to the client, 'When we bring you candidates, we present them to you fully—we give you the good, the bad, and the ugly.' We all have good, bad, and ugly sides to us. I've not met a candidate yet who's perfect. And I've not had a client yet that's the perfect institution, that doesn't have some problems, that doesn't have its own good, bad, and ugly."

Doody continued: "We may not give confidential hospital information, such as a copy of their strategic plan, or budgets, or things like that on the first visit, until we've had a chance to meet with the candidate and assess their level of interest, and make a determination on our part that, 'Yes, this might be a possibility; this might be somebody who could fit.'"

Here's what else you can expect from recruiters:

- They'll arrange your visits to the prospective setting and line up interviews for you with other physicians, administrators, and community leaders.

- Search consultants will try to get to know you—not only your professional interests but also your personal interests. They're "schmooze" experts, adept at personal conversation. In part, this is a mutual screening tool; if your passion is, say, Italian opera, and they represent an organization in rural Michigan, you'll both know it may not be worth pursuing a position at that particular location. But mostly, the conversations are a way to build relationships.

- They may recruit your whole family, particularly if you're relocating. To ease your transition, they may help your spouse explore employment or educational opportunities in the new location; they may even talk to your children about their interests—and their needs in the new location.

- If your work environment will be a hospital, the recruiters (whether they're from an in-house recruitment department or an "outside" search firm) can provide you with current data about the hospital's financial health and set up meetings for you with the medical staff, the chief administrator, hospital board members, hospital volunteers, and others. The recruiters may even set up meetings with supporters in the community, such as bankers, chamber of commerce representatives, and real-estate agents.

What are the disadvantages of using a search firm?

One hazard is that you become a more expensive commodity to the hiring organization, because it of course pays the search firm's fee. According to Bonds and Pulliam,[7] the average agency search costs the hiring organization between $15,000 and $25,000, *plus expenses.*

If you use a search firm, instruct them not to contact the specific companies you'd planned to interview with on your own. (Typically, to avoid duplication, recruiters will ask a candidate whether he or she has submitted applications to potential employers.)

Preparing for Interviews

Preparing for an interview basically means anticipating questions you may be asked and thinking through your responses. (Some people find it helpful to say the answers out loud to themselves, particularly if talking about themselves usually makes them uncomfortable. You can also enlist the help of a friend or your spouse; he or she can ask you sample questions and you can practice responding.) Also practice your people skills: making eye contact, offering a firm handshake, and so on. Many career counselors offer a videotape service: they'll conduct a mock interview with you on camera and evaluate with you how you came across. For example, they might point out contradictions between what you're saying and what your body language is communicating.

Be prepared to answer personal questions, such as why you chose your specialty and why you're making this change. It goes without saying that you'll answer questions honestly. But don't forget that this is, in essence, a sales opportunity: your goal is to persuade the interviewer that you're the best candidate for the position. Although it's not OK to misrepresent the facts, putting a positive spin on things is appropriate. For example, if, as a pediatrician in group practice, you're in conflict with your colleagues, patients are leaving the practice, and the stress from your job is showing up in negative ways in your personal life, you might share some of that with the interviewer—but you also might talk about how the challenges of your current situation have helped you define what you want from your career.

Once you've established contact with a search consultant or prospective employer, follow through by returning his or her phone calls, even if it's to explain that you're not interested at this time.

What to Do When You Receive an Offer

Ask the prospective employer for a letter of intent, and have the letter reviewed by your attorney. If the organization doesn't generate a letter of intent, you and your attorney should generate one. A letter of intent doesn't commit you to the organization or vice versa, but it demonstrates that both parties are serious about negotiating, and it gives you time to get to know each other.

If the organization doesn't offer a letter of intent, it doesn't necessarily mean that they're not interested in you as a good candidate. It may simply mean that they don't have their act together as recruiters. Like people in any job, some do it better than others.

Employment Contracts

Because legal issues are beyond our ken, we'll limit our advice regarding employment contracts to this: you've got to have one, and your lawyer should review it. A family practitioner who was wise enough to get the terms of his employment in writing remembers a colleague's less fortunate experience: His first day at the hospital he heard another new physician complaining because they "had promised her something and were now reneging." Don't let it happen to you. The contract should spell out what the employer has promised you: certain hours at a certain wage.

Tying Up the Loose Ends: Practice Transfer

How the physician handles patient relationships when closing or selling his or her practice is important not only to the patients' psychological well-being but also to the health of the practice being transferred. Out of simple consideration, the physician should notify every patient—usually through a letter that is mailed about 4 weeks before the physician leaves. The physician might also want to telephone some long-term patients. The letter should convey the physician's decision to leave the practice and express affection and gratitude to patients for their loyalty. (In a large group-practice setting, such a letter may not be necessary, because these practices routinely announce the addition of a new physician through the media and in patient newsletters.)

When the physician is selling the practice to another physician, the patient letter fulfills another agenda: it offers an opportunity for the departing physician to introduce the new physician to the patients. The quality of the physician's relationships with his or her patients and the resultant "goodwill" he or she enjoys directly affects the value of the medical practice—and its sales price. It's important to not let that goodwill lapse at the time of sale. A well-worded letter will help transfer the "halo" of goodwill from seller to buyer.

Once you embark on your new career—whether it's clinical or nonclinical, whether it's brand-new or an updated version of what you were doing before—

remember this final and ongoing part of the process: pass on to others what you've learned. Make yourself available to other career changers and dissatisfied doctors. Share your experience, offer support and encouragement, and let them know that they, too, will survive the exciting and anxiety-provoking process called a "career change."

Notes to Part 3

1. Bonds RG, Pulliam KA. *Physician Recruitment and Retention: Practical Techniques for Exceptional Results.* Chicago, Ill: American Hospital Publishing Inc; 1991:9.

2. Ibid, 10.

3. Ibid, xiii.

4. Ibid, xiv.

5. Ibid, 11.

6. Bonds, 17.

7. Bonds, 31.

Appendix 1
Bibliography

American College of Physician Executives. *New Leadership in Health Care Management: The Physician Executive.* 2nd ed. Tampa, Fla: American College of Physician Executives; 1994.

American Medical Association. *Capitation: The Physician's Guide.* Chicago, Ill: American Medical Association; 1995.

American Medical Association. *Managing Managed Care in the Medical Practice.* Chicago, Ill: American Medical Association; 1995.

American Medical Association. *Implementing a Physician Organization.* Chicago, Ill: American Medical Association; 1995.

American Medical Association. *Managing the Medical Practice.* Chicago, Ill: American Medical Association; 1995.

American Medical Association. *Managed Care Strategies for Physicians.* Chicago, Ill: American Medical Association; 1993.

Arron DL. *Running From the Law: Why Good Lawyers Are Getting Out of the Legal Profession.* Berkeley, Calif: Ten Speed Press; 1991. This book may be useful to physicians even though its target audience is lawyers. See in particular appendix 1, "Career Planning Tips."

Aspen Health Law Center Staff. *Legal Answer Book for Managed Care.* Gaithersburg, Md: Aspen Publishers; 1995.

Ball B. *Manage Your Own Career: A Self-Help Guide to Career Choice & Change.* Beekman Publishers; 1989.

Banning K, Friday A. *Planning Your Career Change.* Lincolnwood, Ill: NTC Publishing Group; 1995.

Banning K, Friday A. *How to Change Your Career.* Lincolnwood, Ill: NTC Publishing Group; 1993.

Bernstein AL. *The One Hundred Ninety-One Best Practice Building Strategies for Today's Physician.* Chicago, Ill: Mosby-Year Book; 1987.

Bloomberg M, Mohlie S, eds. *Physicians in Managed Care: A Career Guide.* Tampa, Fla: American College of Physician Executives; 1994.

Bodner J. *Change Your Tune & End the Career Blues: Strategies to Harmonize Lifestyle Career Goals.* Longmeadow Press; 1994.

Bonds R, Pulliam KA. *Physician Recruitment and Retention: Practical Techniques for Exceptional Results.* Chicago, Ill: American Hospital Publishing Inc; 1991. Although geared toward recruiters, not candidates, this book provides the physician job candidate with a behind-the-scenes look at the recruitment process and thus can better prepare him or her for successful interactions. Note, in particular, chapter 6, "Reviewing Legal Issues."

Browning CH, Browning BJ. *How to Partner With Managed Care: A Do-It-Yourself Kit for Building Working Relationships & Getting Steady Referrals.* Duncliff's International; 1994.

Curry W. *Roads to Medical Management: Physician Executives' Career Decisions.* Tampa, Fla: American College of Physician Executives; 1988. Now out of print, this book contains personal accounts of 15 physicians who went into medical management.

Danzi JT. *Positioning Your Practice for the Managed Care Market.* Baltimore, Md: Williams & Wilkins; 1995.

Davis J, Freeman MA. *Marketing for Therapists: A Handbook for Success in Managed Care.* San Francisco, Calif: Jossey-Bass; 1996.

Fischer-Williams M. *Emotions of a Physician.* Gearhart-Edwards Press; 1993.

Gerberg B. *An Easier Way to Change Jobs 1996.* 2nd ed. Princeton Masters Press; 1995.

Hafferty FW, McKinlay JB, eds. *The Changing Character of the Medical Profession: An International Perspective.* New York, NY: Oxford University Press; 1993.

Hammon JL. *Fundamentals of Medical Management: A Guide for the Physician Executive.* Tampa, Fla: American College of Physician Executives; 1993.

Helfand DP. *Career Change.* Lincolnwood, Ill: NTC Publishing Group; 1995.

Hill J. *How to Attain a Lucrative Career in Medical-Pharmaceutical Sales.* Med Sales Pro Publications; 1989.

Kanchier C. *Dare to Change Your Job and Your Life.* MasterMedia Ltd; 1991.

Kennedy MM, Curry W, ed. *Get the Job You Want and the Money You're Worth.* 2nd ed. Tampa, Fla: American College of Physician Executives; 1989.

Krannich RL. *Change Your Job, Change Your Life! High Impact Strategies for Finding Great Jobs in the 90s.* 5th ed. Impact Publications; 1995.

Lazarus A, ed. *Controversies in Managed Mental Health Care.* Washington, DC: American Psychiatric Press; 1996.

Linney GE Jr, Linney BJ. *Medical Directors: What, Why, How?* Tampa, Fla: American College of Physician Executives; 1993.

Morreim EH. *Balancing Act: The New Medical Ethics of Medicine's New Economics.* Washington, DC: Georgetown University Press; 1994.

Moseley GB. *The Physician's Legal Guide to Managed Care.* New York, NY: McGraw-Hill Healthcare Management Group; 1996.

Nash DB, ed. *The Physician's Guide to Managed Care.* Gaithersburg, Md: Aspen Publishers; 1993.

Peters RM. *When Physicians Fail as Managers: An Exploratory Analysis of Career Change Problems.* Tampa, Fla: American College of Physician Executives; 1994.

Rucker TD, Keller MD. *Careers in Medicine: Traditional & Alternative Opportunities.* Garrett Park, Md: Garrett Park Press; 1990. Source of the list of nonpractitioner positions held by medical graduates in Appendix 2.

Shlian DM, ed. *Women in Medicine & Management: A Mentoring Guide.* Tampa, Fla: American College of Physician Executives; 1995.

Titran CG. *How to Get a High-Paying Job in Medical Sales.* RTI Ltd; 1991.

Todd T, Forman BD, ed. *Surviving & Prospering in the Managed Mental Health Care Marketplace.* Professional Resource Exchange; 1994.

Torras H, Lyle JR. *Physicians Guide to Managed Care.* 2nd ed. HealthCare Consultants; 1995.

Tsang R, Oh W. *Beginning an Academic Medical Career: Research, Writing, Speaking.* Hanley & Belfus; 1993.

Turner R, Butcher TE; Reitt B, ed. *Whirlwind — A Doctor's Odyssey From Addiction: Recovery & Help for Others.* Valet Publishing; 1992.

Yanda RL. *Doctors as Managers of Health Teams: A Career Guide for Hospital-Based Physicians.* Books on Demand; 1976.

Yeager NM. *The Career Doctor: Preventing, Diagnosing & Curing Fifty Ailments That Can Threaten Your Career.* New York, NY: John Wiley & Sons; 1991.

Zablocki E. *Changing Physician Practice Patterns: Strategies for Success in a Capitated Health Care System.* Gaithersburg, Md: Aspen Publishers; 1995.

Appendix 2
Nonpractitioner Positions Held by Medical School Graduates*

1. Business/Industry

Advertising & Communications

Chairman, Medicine Department

Director of Medical Affairs

Director of Medical & Legal Affairs

Exec. VP

Exec. VP for Medical Affairs, HSN

Medical Director (8)

President

President, Chinese Computer Communications

Project Director

Sr. VP, Director of Medical & Scientific Affairs

Sr. VP, Group Medical Doctor

Sr. VP & Director of Medical Services

Sr. VP & Medical Director

VP & Associate Medical Director

VP, Director of Medical Affairs

VP for Medical Affairs, Lifetime

Pharmaceutical Manufacturing

Assistant VP & Director of Professional & Marketing Services

Associate Director of Medical Research

Associate Director of Medical Services

Associate Medical Director

Chairman of the Board

Chairman of the Board and President

Clinical Monitor, Research & Development Division, Corporate VP

Director

Clinical Pharmacology

Government Medical Affairs

Medical & Clinical Investigation

Medical Research, Marketed Products, Clinical Investigation Division

New Product Planning (or Development)

Product Development

Professional Communications

Professional Services

Regulatory Affairs

Director of CNS Clinical Research

Director of Clinical Research

Director of Development

Director of Field Sales Administration

Director of Medical Affairs (or Services)

Exec. Director, Biology Research

Exec. Director, Clinical Pharmacology

Exec. Director, Medical Division

Exec. Director, Virus & Cell Biology

Exec. VP

Exec. VP of Pharmaceutical R&D, Quality Control and Medical Activities

Exec. VP Research & Development

Group Manager, Clinical, Epidemiology & Biostatistics

Group Product Manager

Group Research Manager, Medical Affairs

Group VP

Head, Department of Clinical Research

Head, Department of Product Surveillance & Epidemiology

International Medical Liaison

Manager, Business Development, Surgical Products Division

Manager, Medical Investigation & Field Surveillance

* From *Careers in Medicine: Traditional and Alternative Opportunities,* Revised Edition. Rucker, T. Donald, and Keller, Martin D., eds. Garrett Park, MD: Garrett Park Press; 1990. Reprinted with permission.

Medical Director, Corporate Regulatory Affairs

Medical Director, Hospital Products Division

President (10)

President, Health Care Group

President, Research Laboratories

Research Director

Scientific Director

Sr. Director, Clinical Pharmacology— Domestic

Sr. Director, Clinical Pharmacology, Int.

Sr. Exec. VP

Sr. Vice President

Sr. VP, Researching & Development

Sr. VP, Scientific Affairs

VP & Medical Director, Corporate Regulatory Affairs

VP & Head, Molecular Biology Department

VP & Medical Director

VP & Medical Director—Worldwide

Vice President

  Anti-Cancer Research

  Clinical Affairs (or Clinical Research)

  Corporation Medical & Scientific Affairs

  Dermatology, Pharmaceutical R&D Div.

  External Affairs

  Medical (or Medical Affairs)

  Medical and Research & Development

  Medical & Scientific Affairs

  Medical Research

  Medical Services

  New Product Development

  Regulatory Affairs

  Regulatory & Technical Affairs

  Research

  Research & Scientific Affairs

Publishing

Chairman, Editorial Board

Chairman and Chief Exec. Officer, Times Mirror Corp.

Chairman and Publisher

Director, Scientific Publication Division

Editor (33). Also Assistant; Book Review; Coeditor; Corresponding; Cover; Deputy; Managing; Medical; Senior

Editorial Director (11)

Editor-in-Chief; Chief Editor (30)

Editorial Writer

Exec. Director

International Editor

International Publisher

Medical Correspondent, *NY Times*

President

President (publishers' representative)

Publisher (newsletter on investment advice)

Publisher

Publishing Director & Editor

Other

Consultant (unspecified)

Consultant, Drug Regulatory Affairs

Corporate Manager of Environmental Health, IBM Corp.

Director, Employee Health & Safety (large textile manufacturer)

Director, Health Care Development (diversified conglomerate)

Director, Health Care Practice (large accounting firm)

Director, Medical Affairs (large chemical company)

Exec. Director, Institute for Health Planning

Exec. President & Medical Director, International Medical Services, Inc.

Medical Admin. (large manufacturing firm)

Medical Director (many manufacturing firms)

Medical Director (life insur. co.) (700)

Medical Director, Legislative & Regulatory Health Affairs (natural resources co.)

President, Hospital Corporation of America

President, LA Medical Mutual Ins.

President (major oil company)

President (many life insurance companies)

President, Medical Coding Systems, Inc.

President, Oxford Research International

President, Simborg Systems Corp.

President (personnel search firm)

Regional Director, Life Extension Institute

Sr. VP, Hyatt Medical Management Services

Specialist, Health Services Evaluation (systems consulting company)

VP, Advanced Business Development (large medical equipment & supply company)

VP, R&D (computer-software firm)

2. Certification & Accreditation

Joint Commission on Accreditation of Hospitals

Assistant VP

President

VP for Accreditation

VP for Education

VP for External Affairs

National Board of Medical Examiners

President and Director

Sr. Medical Evaluation Officer (3)

VP for Evaluation Programs

Chief Exec. Officer, American Board...(10)

VP, Federation of State Medical Boards

3. Charitable Foundation/ Voluntary Health Org.

Deputy Director, Division of Health Sciences, Rockefeller Foundation

Director of Medical Services, National Foundation for Infantile Paralysis

Exec. Director, National Interagency Council on Smoking & Health (NYC)

Exec. VP (2)

President (charitable foundation) (3)

President (voluntary health organization)

Project Director, Inter-Society Commission for Heart Disease Resources

Scientific Director, The National Foundation for Cancer Research

Sr. VP for Research, Am. Cancer Society

Special Advisor to the President
  (charitable foundation)
VP, The Commonwealth Fund

4. Education

Medical School—
Officials & Administrative Staff
(by functional area)

Academic Affairs
  Association Dean (35)
  Dean
  Vice-Chancellor
Academic & Research Affairs—Assoc.
  Dean
Administration—Asst./Assoc. Dean for
  (9)
Admissions—Asst./Assoc. Dean;
  Chairman or Director (32)
Admissions & Curriculum—Associate
  Dean
Affiliated Programs—Associate Dean (3)
Allied Health Professional Training—
  Assistant/Associate Dean/Director (5)
Alumni Affairs—Asst. Dean/VP or
  Director
Alumni Affairs & CME Coordinator
Ambulatory Affairs—Associate Dean (2)
Area Health Education Center—Assoc.
  Dean
Basic Sciences—Assistant/Associate
  Dean/Coordinator
BA/MD Programs—Assistant Dean
Biomedical Graduate Studies—Assoc.
  Dean
Brookhaven National Lab.—Clinical Dean

CEO (Dean, President, etc) (113)
Clinical Affairs—Asst. Dean or Dean (47)
Continuing Medical Education—Assistant
  or Associate Dean (74); Coordinator or
  Director (4)
Council on Health Programs—Chairman
Curriculum—Asst./Assoc. Dean (17)
Development—Associate Dean
Education—Assistant Dean
Extended Medical Programs—Assoc.
  Dean (2)
Extramural Affairs—Asst./Assoc. Dean
  (3)
Faculty Affairs—Associate Dean
Faculty Council—Chairman
Geriatric Medicine—Associate Dean
Gerontology & Community Med./Assoc.
  Dean
Government Affairs—Assistant Dean
Graduate Medical Education—Asst./
  Assoc. Dean (11)
Graduate & Continuing Medical
  Education—Associate Dean
Health Affairs—Associate Provost & Dean
Hospital Affairs (Program)—Asst./Assoc.
  Dean (52)
Human Subjects Protection—Asst. Dean
  (2)
Interinstitutional Programs—Associate
  Dean (3)
International Programs—Associate Dean
  or Chairman (3)
Local Med. Center—Asst./ Assoc. Dean
  (22)
Medical Director of Faculty Practice
  Plan—Associate Dean
Medical Education—Associate Dean
Medical Education & Curr.—Assoc. Dean

Minority Affairs—Assistant/Associate Dean/Coordinator (7)

Naval Regional Medical Center—Assoc. Dean

Patient Care—Associate Dean

Planning—Assistant Dean

Planning & Development—Assist. to the VP/Associate Dean (2)

Planning & Operations—Associate Dean

Postdoctoral Programs—Assoc. Dean/ Director

Postdoctoral Programs & Faculty Development—Assistant Dean

Preprofessional Education—Associate Dean

Public Health—Associate Dean

Publications—Head, Section on

Research—Assistant or Associate Dean (11)

Research Development (Neuroscience)— Associate Dean

Residency Affairs—Coordinator

Rural Health—Assistant Dean

Rural Health Education—Associate Dean

Scientific Affairs—Associate Dean

Special Projects—Asst./Assoc. Dean (5)

Student Affairs—Asst./ Assoc. Dean (71)

Student Affairs & Admin.—Assoc. Dean

Student Affairs & Alumni Affairs— Associate (2)

Student & Curriculum Affairs—Associate Dean (11)

Student & Graduate Medical Affairs— Senior Associate Dean

Surgical Sciences & Services—Assoc. Dean

Undergraduate Medical Education— Assistant/Deputy Dean

VA Medical Center—Asst./Assoc. Dean (30)

VA Research—Assistant Dean

Veterans Affairs—Asst./Assoc. Dean (13)

Medical School— Officials & Administrative Staff (by title)

Academic Advisor

Assistant Dean (2)

   Area Health Education Center (5)

   for Air Force Affairs

   for Ed. Programs, University Hospital (2)

   for a given class in Medical School (3)

   for Research, Budget, & Fiscal Affairs

Assistant to the Dean

Assistant to the Vice-Chancellor for Medical Affairs

Associate/Executive/Deputy Dean (53)

Associate Dean—Community Services

Associate Dean—Health Services

Assoc. Dean/Coord.—Satellite Campuses (8)

Associate Director

   Internal Director

   Medical & Laboratory Specialization

   Research Training & Degree Programs

Dean for Medical Services

Dean, School of Basic Medical Science

Director

   Ambulatory Education Programs

   Cancer Center (2)

   Center for Educational Resources

   Center for Health Services & Policy Res.

   Community Health Centers

   CME & Audio-Visual Coordinator

Health Policy & Management, Division
   of Environmental Sciences Laboratory
Institute for Health Policy Studies
Institute for Medical Humanities
Medical Center
Medical Scientist Training Program
Program in Behavioral Science, School
   of Biomedical Education
Program in Health Services Evaluation
Program in History of Medicine
Research in Medical Education, Division
Respiratory Studies, Division of
Sports Medicine Center
The Marine Biomedical Institute
University (Student) Health Services (4)
President of the Medical Center & Vice-
   Chancellor for Medical Affairs
Special Assistant to the Dean
Special Assistant to the Dean, Binational
   Health Programs (2)
Vice-Chancellor, Health Sciences & Dean

Medical School—Basic Science Unit

(Department/Division/Section with Chair
   held by MD. In many of these units,
   other faculty positions are also held by
   MDs)*
Anatomy
Biological Chemistry
Biomedical Engineering
Biometry
Blood Bank Transfusion
Cell Biology
Center for Brain Research
Clinical Chemistry
Community Medicine

Diagnostic Nuclear Medicine
Environmental Health
Epidemiology & International Health
Genetics (Human Genetics)
Health Computer Sciences
History of Medicine (Health Sciences)
Immunology/Microbiology
Laboratory Hematology
Medical Biology
Medical Biophysics & Computing
Medical Physics (Professor of)
Medical Statistics & Epidemiology
Microbiology
Molecular Biophysics & Biochemistry
Neuroanatomy
Neurobiology
Neuroscience
Pathology
   Autopsy Service
   Clinical
   Cytopathology
   Experimental Pathology
   Forensic Medicine
   Immunopathology
   Laboratory Medicine
   Medical Technology
   Neuro-pathology
   Surgical Pathology
Pharmacology
   Clinical Pharmacology
   Laboratory of Applied Pharmacokinetics
   Molecular Pharmacology
   Pharmacology & Nutrition
   Pharmacology & Therapeutics
   Psychopharmacology

---

* Faculty in some basic sciences, as well as the clinical sciences, follow dual careers when they
teach students and treat patients. Moreover, many often engage in research.

Physiology

Physiology & Biophysics

Preventive Medicine & Biometrics

Public Health

Radiation Biology & Biophysics

Regional Laboratory Services

Social Medicine & Health Policy

Tropical Medicine & Medical Microbiology

Positions in Health Sciences but External to the Medical School

College of Chiropractic

Asst. Prof. Basic & Clinical Science

Assistant Professor of Clinical Science

Associate Professor of Basic Science & Clinical Science

School of Pharmacy

Asst. Clinical Prof. of Medical Science

Associate Prof. of Clinical Pharmacy (15)

Associate Prof. of Human Pathology (2)

Dean and Professor of Physiology

Research Assist. Professor of Pharmacology

School of Public Health

Assoc. Prof., Health Policy & Admin.

Dean (or Associate, or Assistant)

Dir., Ctr. for Analysis of Health Practices

Director, Community Health Sciences

Director, Inst. for Health Research

Professor of Health Administration

Professor of Medical Care Organization

Res. Prof. of Public Health Administration & Chairman, Dept. of Field Training

Faculty Positions External to the Health Sciences*

Associate Professor of Psychiatry & Religion, Yale Divinity School

Director of Sport Medicine, U.S. Sport Academy

Professor, J. F. Kennedy School of Government, Harvard University

Research Associate, Conservation of Human Resources Program, Columbia University

Visit. Assoc. Prof. of Law, NYU Law School

University Officer

Act. Coordinator, Minority Student Affairs

Assistant Dean for Long-Range Planning

Assistant Vice Chancellor for VA Affairs

Asst./Assoc. VP for Health (or Med.) Affairs

Assistant VP for Interinstitutional Affairs

Assistant VP for Affiliated Institutions

Chairman, Board of Governors, Mayo Clinic

Chancellor (8)

Consultant—to Provost or Chancellor (2)

Director, Center for Human Growth & Development

Director, Continuing Health Professional Education, Medical Center

Director of the Medical Center

Dean

Health Program Advisor

President (6)

---

* One study covering the period 1980–1981 found more than 100 physicians employed in academia outside the medical school.

Senior Vice President (2)

Special Assistant to the President

Vice Chancellor for Academic Affairs

Vice Chancellor for Health Affairs (2)

Vice Chancellor for Health Affairs, Ohio
Board of Regents

Vice President (3)

for Academic Affairs

for Clinical Affairs

for Health Affairs (Health Sciences/
Medical Affairs/Medical Center) (34)

for Hospital Affairs

for Interinstitutional Affairs

5. Government—Federal

Congress

Asst. Dir., Office of Technology
Assessment

Congressional Science Fellow (sponsored
by Federation of American Societies for
Experimental Biology)

Counsel, Subcommittee on Health &
Environment, Committee on Energy &
Commerce, U.S. House of
Representatives

Exec. Director, Prospective Assessment
Commission, OTA

Manager of Health Program Analysis, OTA

Member, U.S. House of Representatives

Professional Staff Member

Committee on Energy & Commerce,
House

Committee on Interstate & Foreign
Commerce, House

Project Director, Gentics, OTA

Staff Director, Sub-Committee on Health
& Science Research, Senate

Department of Defense—Staff

Assistant Secretary of Defense (Health
Affairs)

Dean, School of Medicine, United States
University of the Health Sciences

Deputy Assistant Secretary of Defense for
Health Resources & Programs

Director, Office of Civilian Health &
Medical Programs Uniformed Services

Special Assistant for Medical Readiness

Special Asst. for Professional Activities

Department of Defense—US Air Force

Administrative Positions

Aerospace Medical Division Commander

Aerospace Medical Research Laboratory

Air Force Med. Service Center
Commander

Air Force Inspection & Safety Command
(7)

CHAMPUS (Civilian Health Program)

Major Command Surgeons (13)

Military Enlistment Processing Command

Office of Secretary of Defense (Health
Affairs)

Office of the Surgeon General (6)

Tri-Service Medical Information Systems
Program Office

USAF School of Aerospace Med.
Commander

Consultant Positions

Air Force Medical Service Center (10)
Major Command Surgeon Offices (21)

Research & Development Positions

Aerospace Medical Research Laboratory (7)
Aeronautical Systems Division
Armed Forces Radiological Research
Armed Forces Institute of Pathology

Teaching Positions

School of Health Care Sciences (4)
Uniformed Services University of Health Sciences (8)
USAF School of Aerospace Medicine (5)

Other Positions

Air Force Manpower & Personnel Center Physical Evaluation Board (8)
Air Force Board for Correction of Military Records (2)
Aerospace Medical Division (AMD), Clinical Sciences Division (22)
AMD Epidemiology Division (2)
AMD Crew Technology Division (2)
AMD Hyperbaric Medicine Division (3)
AMD Occupational & Envir. Health Lab.
DoD Medical Examination Review Board (2)

Department of Defense—US Army

Chief of Training & Education, Aeromedical Activity, Ft. Rucker, AL

Department of Defense—US Navy

Commanding Officer
National Naval Medical Center
Naval Hospital (3)
Naval Aerospace Medical Institute
Naval Aerospace Medical Research Lab
Naval Air Regional Medical Center
Naval Biodynamics Laboratory
Naval Environmental Health Center
Naval Regional Medical Center (2)
Naval Medical Research Institute
Naval Medical Research Unit, Cairo, EG
Naval Submarine Medical Research Lab

Bureau of Medicine & Surgery

Assistant Chief for Health Care Programs
Assistant Chief for Planning & Resources
Assist. Chief for Professional Development
Deputy Director, Medical Corps Division
Deputy Surgeon General, Deputy Chief
Director, Contingency Planning Division
Director, Education & Training Division
Director, Medical Corps Division
Director, Program Operations Division
Officer-in-charge, Naval Undersea Medical Institute
Inspector General, Medical
Surgeon General/Chief

Other Staff Positions

Assistant for Medical Corps Officer, Distribution/Placement, Naval Military Personnel Command

Assistant for Medical Corps Officer/ Warrant Officer Distribution/Placement, Naval Military Personnel Command

Director, Med. Programs, Headquarters, USMC

Director, Professional Activities, Office of the Secretary of Defense

Fleet Med. Officer, Comd., Train. Command

Force Surgeon, Headquarters, Fleet Marine Force (2)

Head, Prof. Div., Chief of Naval Operations

Primary Care Medical Officer, Headquarters Fleet Marine Force

Staff Dir., Defense Medical Material Board

Staff Medical Officer/Medical Advisor, Headquarters, USMC

Staff Medical Officer/Fleet Surgeon, Commander in Chief, Pacific Fleet

Staff Medical Officer, London, England

Department of Health & Human Services

Secretary

Office of Assistant Secretary for Planning & Evaluation

Assistant Sec. for Planning & Evaluation

Deputy Asst. Sec. for Planning & Evaluation

Office of Assistant Secretary for Health: Public Health Service

Assistant Secretary for Health

Deputy Asst. Sec. Disease Prevention

Deputy Assistant Secretary for Health

Deputy Asst. Sec. for International Health

Deputy Asst. Sec. for Population Affairs

Director
  Health Planning
  National Immunization Initiative Program
  Office of Adolescent Pregnancy Program
  Office of Child Health Affairs
  Office of Health Info. & Health Promotion
  Office of Health Practice Assessment
  Office of Health Technology
  Office of International Health
  Office of Smoking and Health
  Special Health Initiatives

Science, Advisor, Deputy Asst. Sec. for Health Policy, Research & Statistics

Special Assistant for External Affairs

Special Assistant for the Asst. Sec. (3)

Surgeon General

National Center for Health Services Research

Director

Associate Deputy Director for Medical & Scientific Affairs

Associate Director, Professional Services

Director, Division of Extramural Research

Director, Division of Intramural Research

Executive Secretary, Health Care Technology Study Section

Exec. Sec., Health Services Research Review

National Center for Health Statistics

Director

Director, Health Examination Statistics

Medical Advisor

Nutrition Advisor

Alcohol, Drug Abuse & Mental Health Administration

Administrator

Assistant Administrator for Agency Goals

National Institute of Mental Health

Director

Director, The Staff College

Deputy Director, NIMH

Special Assistant to the Director

Director of Extramural Project Review

Deputy, Extramural Project Review

Chief, Applied & Social Project Review
Branch

Chief, Basic Research Review Branch

Chief, Clin. & Ser. Develop. Review
Branch

Chief, Clin. Manpower Develop. Review
Br.

Chief, Research Development Review
Branch

Director, Div. of Biometry & Epidemiology

Chief, Demography & Epidemiology
Branch

Director, Div. of Extramural Res.
Programs

Deputy Director, Division of Extramural
Research Programs

Chief, Research Scientist Develop.
Section

Chief, Small Grants Section

Chief, Clinical Research Branch

Chief, Center for Studies of Schizophrenia

Chief, Psychopharmacology Research
Branch

Director, Div. of Manpower & Training

Associate Director of Research Training,
Division of Manpower & Training

Chief, Psychiatry Education Branch

Chief, Center for State Mental Health
Manpower Development

Training Specialist

Director, Div. Mental Health Programs

Deputy Director

Associate Director

Chief, Community Mental Health
Services Support

Chief, Mental Health Services Support

Chief, Mental Health Study Center

Director, Div. Sp. Mental Health Programs

Deputy Director

Chief, Center for Minority Group Mental
Health Programs

Chief, Center for Studies of Mental
Health of the Aging

Chief, Disaster Assistance & Emergency
Mental Health Section

Chief, National Center for Prevention &
Control of Rape

Centers for Disease Control and Prevention (Atlanta, GA)

Director

Assistant Director for International
Health

Asst. Director for Public Health Practice

Assistant Director for Science

Assistant Director, Interagency Affairs

Assistant Director/Washington

Director, Bureau of Epidemiology

Director, Bureau of Laboratories

Director, Bureau of Smallpox Eradication

Director, Bureau of Training

Director, Bureau of Tropical Diseases
   Chief, Vector Biology & Control Division

Director, National Institute of
   Occupational Safety & Health

Assistant to the Director

Director, Office of Extramural
   Coordination & Special Projects

Director, Division of Respiratory Disease
   Studies

Director, Division of Safety Research

Director, Division of Criteria
   Documentation & Standards
   Development

Director, Division of Surveillance Hazard
   Evaluations & Field Studies

Director, Division of Biomedical and
   Behavioral Sciences

Director, Division of Training &
   Manpower Development

Medical Officer, Office of Program
   Planning & Evaluation

Director, Nutrition Division, Center for
   Health Promotion & Education

Food & Drug Administration

Commissioner

Deputy Commissioner

Associate Commissioner for Health Affairs
   Director, Medical Review Staff

Associate Commissioner for Medical
   Affairs
   Deputy Associate Commissioner for
      Medical Affairs

Associate Commissioner for Science

Assistant Commissioner for Professional
   & Consumer Programs

Director, Orphan Products Development

Medical Officer, International Affairs

Center for Drugs & Biologics

Director

Scientific Director

Office of Drug Standards

Director

Deputy Director—Medical Affairs

Deputy Assoc. Director for Drug
   Monographs

Director, Anti-Infective Products Division

Director, Cardio-Renal Products Division

Director, Surgical-Dental Products
   Division

Director, Metabolism and Endocrine
   Division

Director, Neuropharmacological Products
   Division

Director, Oncology &
   Radiopharmaceutical Products Division

Office of Drugs

Deputy Director

Director, Division of Drug Use Experience

Office of Drug Review & Investigation

Director, Div. of Scientific Investigations
Chief, Clinical Investigation Branch
Chief, Non-Clinical Labs. Studies Branch

Center for Devices & Radiological Health

Director, Office of Health Affairs

Office of Biologics

Director
Director, Division of Bacterial Products
Director, Division of Biologics Evaluation
Director, Div. of Blood & Blood Products
Director, Div. of Product Quality Control
Director, Division of Virology

Office of Medical Devices

Assoc. Director for Health Affairs

Office of Radiological Health

Director, Office of Health Affairs

Bureau of Foods

Associate Director for Sciences, Division of Pathology
Associate Director for Nutrition & Consumer Sciences
Special Assistant for Medical Affairs

Health Resources & Services Administration

Director, Office of Graduate Medical Ed.

Bureau of Health Professions

Deputy Director
Deputy Director, Division of Associated Health Professions
Deputy Director, Division of Health Professions Training Support
Deputy Director, Division of Health Professions Analysis
Director, Division of Medicine

Bureau of Health Planning

Medical Advisor

Health Services Administration

Administrator
Special Assistant to the Administrator

Bureau of Health Care Delivery

Director
Associate Bureau Director, Program for Maternal & Child Health
Chief, Rehabilitative Services Branch
Chief, Genetic Disease Services Branch
Chief, Research & Training Services Branch
Associate Bureau Director, Program Office for Community Health Centers
Associate Bureau Director, Program Office for National Health Service Corps
Chief, Professional Affairs Branch
Director, National Health Service Corps

Indian Health Service

Director
Deputy Director

Bureau of Medical Services

Director

Deputy Director

Director, Bureau Prisons Medical
Programs

Deputy Director

Director, Division of Hospitals & Clinics

Medical Director, Office of Workers'
Compensation Programs

Director, Division of Federal Employee
Occupational Health

Director, Division of Coast Guard Medical
Services

National Institutes of Health

Director

Deputy Director

Special Assistant to the Director

Director

Division of Computer Research & Tech.

Division of Research Grants

Division of Research Resources

Division of Research Services

Ethics Advisory Board

Fogarty International Center

NIH Clinical Center

Office of Medical Application of
Research

Office for Protection From Research
Risks

Director

Lister Hill National Center for
Biomedical Communications

National Cancer Institute

National Eye Institute

National Heart, Lung and Blood
Institute

National Institute of Allergy & Infectious
Diseases

National Institute of Arthritis,
Metabolism & Digestive Diseases

National Institute of Child Health &
Human Development

National Institute of Environmental
Health Sciences

National Institute of General Medical
Sciences

National Institute of Neurological &
Communicative Disorders & Stroke

National Institute on Aging

National Library of Medicine

Health Care Financing Administration

Associate Administrator for Management
& Support Services

Deputy Director, Office of PSRO, Bureau
of Health Stds. & Quality

Director, Office of Professional &
Scientific Affairs, Office of the
Administrator

Director, Office of Child Health, Office of
Special Programs Deputy Director

Director, Bureau of Health Standards &
Quality

Senior Health Analyst, Office of Research

Rehabilitation Services Administration

Director, Medical Affairs

Social Security Administration

Special Assistant, Office of Program Policy
& Analysis

Regional Offices

Director, Services Delivery Assessment

Director, US Public Health Service Hospital

PSRO Representative

Regional Health Administrator, PHS (10)

Associate Director, Professional Services, NCHSR

Department of State

Deputy Asst. Secretary, Medical Services

Deputy Medical Director

Asst. Medical Director, Environ. Health

Asst. Medical Director, Health Care Program

Asst. Medical Dir., Mental Health Program

Chairman, Tropical Medicine

Director, Domes. Medical Program

Director, Overseas Medical Program

Medical Director, US Foreign Service

Agency for International Development

Acting Director, Office of Health, Bureau for Science & Technology

Chief, Health/Nutrition Division, Bureau of Africa

Health Officer, USAID

Health & Nutrition Officer, USAID

Medical Officer

Chief, Health, Population and Nutrition Division, Bureau for Asia

Chief, Health/Population/Nutrition, USAID Mission

Chief, Health & Family Planning Division

Chief, Office of Health & Nutrition, USAID

Health Development Officer, USAID Mission

Population Officer

Deputy Director, Office of Health, Bureau for Science & Technology

Tropical Disease Office

Chief, Health Services Division

Deputy Director, Office of Population, Bureau for Science & Epidemiology

Medical Officer

Public Health Physician

Director for Health & Population, Bureau for Science & Technology

Veterans Affairs—Central Office

Administrator

Chief Medical Director

Assistant Chairman, Medical Director

Assistant Deputy, Chief Medical Director

Associate Deputy, Chief Medical Director

Assistant Chief Medical Director for

Academic Affairs

Clinical Services

Extended Care

Planning & Program Development

Professional Services

Research & Development

Director

Affiliated Educational Program Service

CE & Staff Development Service

Health Information Systems Associate Director

Health Services R&D Service

Medical Research Service Deputy Director

Director, Mental Health & Behavioral
  Sciences Services
Deputy Director
Associate Director, Alcohol & Drug
  Dependence
Associate Director, Psychiatry
Associate Director, Treatment Services
Director
  Neurology Service
  Nuclear Medicine Service
  Pathology Service
  Radiology Service
  Rehabilitation Service
  Spinal Cord Injury Service
Medical Inspector

Veterans Administration—Field Stations

Associate Chief of Staff for Education
Associate Chief of Staff for Research &
  Development
Chief, Medical/Dental Division
Director, Education Services

Other Federal Government Departments and Agencies

Assistant Secretary, Occupational Safety
  and Health Administration, Dept. of
  Labor
Astronaut, NASA
Chairman, Aeromedical Standards
  Division, FAA, Dept. of Transportation
Chairman, Occupational Health Division,
  FAA
Chairman, Program in Scientific Medical
  Standards, FAA

Chief, Aviation Safety Research Office,
  NASA Ames Research Center
Chief, Aviation Toxicology Laboratory,
  Civil Aeromedical Institute, FAA
Chief, FAA Civil Aeromedical Institute
Chief, Medical Operations, Johnson Space
  Center, NASA
Chief, Medical Operations, Peace Corps
Deputy Director, Office of Sciences &
  Technology, Exec. Office of the President
Director of Gorgas Memorial Laboratory
Director of Life Sciences, NASA
Director of Medical Recruitment, Bureau
  of Prisons, Dept. of Justice
Director of the Woodrow Wilson Int.
  Center, Smithsonian Institution
Exec. Director, National Advisory
  Commission on Health Manpower
Federal Air Surgeon, FAA
Manager, Operational Medicine, NASA
Medical Director, Dept. of Justice
Medical Officer, Division of Disability
  Benefits, Railroad Retirement Board
Mission Specialist, Space Shuttle
  Program, NASA
President, Gorgas Memorial Institute of
  Tropical & Preventive Medicine, Inc.
President, Institute of Medicine
Principal Investigator, Skylab Biomedical
  Experiments, NASA
Regional Medical Director, US Postal
  Service (4)
Scientist-Astronaut, NASA
Special Assistant to the President for
  Health Policy

6. Government—State

Department of Health
(or Equivalent)

Administrator, Division of Health & Medical Services, Dept. of Health & Social Services (WY)

Assistant Comm., Health Care Programs (VA)

Assistant Director, Division of Local Health Services

Assistant Director, Public Health Lab.

Assistant Director, State Hygienic Labs.

Case Control Reviewer, Receiving Hospital

Chief, Bureau of Maternal & Child Care, Dept. of Health & Envir. & Control (SC)

Chief Medical Office & Deputy Director, Health Facilities & Standards & Control, Office of Health Systems Mgt. (NY)

Chief Medical Examiner (NC)

Chief Physician, Bureau of Hospital Services, Office of Health Systems Management (NY)

Chief, Office of Medical Services (SD)

Chief, Research & Statistics Office (HI)

Commissioner (NY, VA, VI)

Commissioner, Dept. of Health & Environmental Control (SC)

Commissioner, Dept. of Human Resources (GA)

Commissioner of Health (CT, NY, OK, TX, VI)

Commissioner of Public Health (TN)

Commissioner & State Registrar, Dept. of Health & Environmental Control (SC)

Deputy Commissioner for Special Health Services (TX)

Deputy Secretary, Dept. of Health & Mental Hygiene (MD)

Deputy Secretary for Community Health Services (PA)

Director—Unspecified

Director

   Crippled Children's Division (SC)

   Dept. of Health Services and State Registrar of Vital Records (AZ)

   Dept. of Health & Envir. Sciences (MT)

   Division of Epidemiology, Bureau of Health Services (KY)

   Division of Health (MO)

   Division of Health Services (NC)

   Division of Planning (PR)

   Division of Physical Health, Dept. of Human Resources (GA)

   Division of Public Health (NH)

   Division of Public Health, Dept. of Health & Social Services (DE)

   Interdisciplinary Research Team, Epidemiology Studies Section (CA)

   of Health, Dept. of Health & Environment (KS, MT)

   of Public Health, Dept. of Human Resources (DC)

   of Public Health, Dept. of Public Health (IL, MI)

   of Health Services Division, Dept. of Social & Health Services (WA)

   of Office of Health Director (Canal Zone)

   of Office of Statistics (MA)

Executive Director (CO, UT)

Exec. Officer, State Board of Health & State Registrar of Vital Statistics (MS)

Physician Consultant, Dept. of Health & Social Services (WI)

Secretary of Health (PA, PR)

Secretary of Health & Mental Hygiene (MD)

Secretary & State Health Commissioner, State Board of Health (IN)

Secretary & State Health Officer, Dept. of Health & Human Resources (LA)

State Commissioner of Health (NJ)

State Director of Health (WV)

State Health Commissioner (VA, VT)

State Health Officer (AL, NV, ND)

State Med. Exam., Division of Health (UT)

Insurance Program Administration (Medicaid, Worker's Compensation)

Administrator, Division of Health & Medical Services, Dept. of Health & Social Services (WY)

Associate Medical Director, Dept. of Income Maintenance (CN)

Chief Medical Director, Dept. of Public Welfare (IN)

Deputy Director, Medicaid Agency (AL)

Medical Consultant, Dept. of Public Welfare (NE)

Medical Consultant, Division of Medical Assistance (CO)

Medical Consultant (county level), Dept. of Social & Health Services (WA)

Medical Director, Dept. of Public Welfare (MA, NE)

Medical Director, Office of Medical Policy & Procedures, Dept. of Social & Health Services (WA)

Member, Medical Review Team, Dept. of Public Welfare (IN)

Mental Health Agency

Administrative Asst., Mental Health Center

Assoc. Com., Office of Mental Health

Chief Exec. Officer (Administrator; Director) Department

Commissioner, Dept. of Mental Health & Mental Retardation (VA)

Director, the Nathan S. Kline Institute for Psychiatric Research

Director, Rockland Research Institute

Director, State Hospital

Director, Research, NY Psychiatric Inst.

Equal Employment Opportunity Officer, Central Office

Hospital Aide, Mental Health Psychiatric Center

Hospital Aide Supervisor, Mental Retardation Development Center

Mental Health Administrator

Dept. in Mental Health Central Office

Local Mental Health & Develop. Center (2)

Mental Health Receiving Hospital

Social Program Coordinator, Mental Health Psychiatric Center

Social Service Worker, Mental Retardation Development Center

Other

Administrative Assistant, Supervisor, Med. Units, Dept. of Human Services (OK)

Administrative Asst., Employment Services

Assemblyman, 9th District (CA)

Chaplain, R & C Correctional Institution

CEO, Medical Board of Regents

Chairman, Exec. Committee, Statewide PSR Council, Inc. (NY)

Commissioner of Public Health, Dept. of Human Services (DC)

Coordinator of Medical Services, Dept. of Social & Rehabilitation Services (KS)

Deputy Commissioner for Programs, Dept. of Human Resources (TX)

Director, State Health Planning Comm. (NW)

Majority Leader, House of Representatives (FL)

Medical Consultant, Dept. of Social Services & Housing (HA)

Medical Consultant, Dept. of Social Rehabilitation Services (RI)

Member, governing board of various departments, such as Education, Health Licensure, Workers Compensation, and Administrative Services

Psychiatrist Consultant, Dept. of Welfare (WV)

Sec., Dept. of Human Resources (KY, NC)

Social Program Coordinator, Dept. of Economic & Commercial Development

Utilization Review Administrator, Dept. of Social & Rehabilitation Services (KS)

Vocal Rehabilitation Counselor, Rehabilitation Services Commission

Youth Ldr. Super., Veteran's Children Home

7. Government—Local

Alcohol/Drug Abuse Coordinator, county

Air Pollution Control Officer, county

Assistant Comm. for Biostatistics, city

Assistant Health Director for Disease Control, county

Assistant Health Officer, county

Assistant Medical Examiner, city

Chief, Acute Communicable Disease, city

Chief Medical Officer, The Fire Dept., city

Chief, Preventive Med. Services Div., county

Commissioner (or Commission of Health), Dept. of Health, city and county

Coroner (or Medical Exam.), city & county

Deputy Commissioner, Health Dept., county

Deputy Director of Health for Personal Health Services

Director

  Community Mental Health Services, county

  Epidemiology, Health Dept., county

  Maternal & Child Health Program, city

  Medical Services, city

Director of Public Health (county health officer)

Director, Dept. of Public Health & Welfare

District Health Officer, city & state

Exec. Director, Health & Hospitals Governing Commissioner, Cook County

Family Planning Officer, county

Head, Communicable Disease Program, county

Health Commissioner, Health Division, city

Health Officer, county

Medical Health Officer, county

Medical Services Officer, city

Mental Health Officer, county

Program Chief, Substance Abuse Service, county

Public Health Director, city

Supervisor, District Health Program, county

Tuberculosis Controller/VD Controller, county

8. Health Care Provider

(Hospital, nursing home, health maintenance organization, etc)

Assistant (or Associate) Director or Administrator

Associate Medical Director, Hospitals & Clinics, Health Sciences Center

Associate Medical Director, Southern California Permanente Medical Group

Chairman & CEO, National Medical Care, Inc.

CEO (Administrator; Director; President)

Corporate Planning Advisor, Kaiser Foundation Health Plan

Director, Frontier Nursing Service

Director, Laboratory Computer Science, Massachusetts General Hospital

Director, Northwest Kidney Center

Director, Program Development, Health Development, Inc.

Director, Research Administration

Director of Medical Education & Director of Quality Assurance

Dept. of Medical Methods Research, Permanente Medical Group, CA

Director

Director, Technology Assessment

Assistant Director, Epidemiology & Biostatistics

Assistant Director, Health Services Research

Executive Director, Development & Public Affairs, The New York Hospital

Exec. Director, Planned Parenthood Clinic

Exec. VP & Dir., Johns Hopkins Hospitals

General Director

Medical Director

Medical Director, HMO

Medical Director, Ohio Masonic Home

Medical Director, Planned Parenthood Clinic

Medical Dir., Reg. Perinatal Center (NJ)

President

President, Geriatric Care Associates

President, Health Activation Systems (Minneapolis)

Regional Dir. of Education & Research, So. CA Region, Kaiser Permanente Medical Gr.

Vice President

General Manager, Kaiser Foundation Hospital Health Plan

New & Emerging Technology, Humana Corp.

Professional & Academic Affairs

for Education & Research

for Medical Affairs (many hospitals)

for Operations, American Health Systems (nursing home group)

for Strategic Planning, American Medical International

9. Health Insurance Program (Private)

Not-for-profit

Medical Director, Blue Shield Plan

Medical Director—HMO operations, Blue Shield Plan

President, Blue Cross Plan

President, Blue Shield Plan

Sr. VP, Blue Cross Plan

Sr. VP & Medical Director, Blue Shield Plan

Sr. VP, Medical & Professional Affairs, Blue Shield Plan

VP, Medical Affairs & Medical Director, BS

VP, Professional Programs

VP and Medical Director

Commercial

Asst. Assoc. or Chief (Medical) Director of
  Accident & Health Claims
  Claims
  Employee Benefits
  Group Claims
  Medical Policy and Program

Senior Medical Consultant

VP and Medical Director

10. Law

(*Note:* Several positions duplicate listings elsewhere in this Table and inadvertently may include some where clinical practice still represents a majority of the individual's time.)

Associate Professor of Emergency Medicine

Associate Professor of Surgery

Attorney (private firm specializing in aviation law)

Chairman, Four Sect. Committees, National Fire Protection Association & President, American College of Legal Medicine

Chief, Division of Medical Legal Research, Dept. of Legal Medicine, Armed Forces Institute of Pathology

Commissioner, Allegheny County

Coroner

Director/Associate Director, Division of Medical-Legal Affairs, VA

Head, Washington Office, American College of Physicians

Mayor of Kansas City

Member/Partner/Owner (law firm)

Professorial Lecturer, The National Law Center, GW University

Senior VP, Medical & Scientific Affairs (large drug firm)

Staff Associate, Division of Forensic Programs, National Inst. Mental Health

Trial Attorney

11. Professional/Trade Associations

American Medical Association

Executive Vice President

VP—Scientific Information

VP—Medical Information & Scient. Policy

Director, Department of Physician Credentials & Qualifications

Assistant Director, Department of Physician Credentials & Qualifications

Director, Department of Undergraduate Medical Evaluation

Assistant Director, Department of Undergraduate Medical Evaluation

Field Rep., Graduate Medical Evaluation

Director, Division of Medical Education

Director, Division of Scientific Analysis & Technology

Assistant Director, Division of Scientific Analysis & Technology

Director, Department of Environmental, Public & Occupational Health

Assistant Director, Department of Environmental, Public & Occupational Health

Director, Division of Drugs & Toxicology

Assistant Director, Division of Drugs

Senior Scientist, Division of Drugs

Director, Dept. of Specialty Journals

Director, Dept. of *JAMA* Editorial Staff

Director, Dept. of *JAMA* Science

Senior Editor—*JAMA*

Association of American Medical Colleges

President

Director, Department of Academic Affairs

Director, Department of Health Services

Director, Department of Planning & Policy Development

Director, Division of Accreditation

Director, Division of Educational Resources & Programs

Special Staff Consultant

Other

Associate Director, American Hospital Association

Associate Executive Director, Int. Health, American Public Health Association

Associate Exec. VP, Membership

Associate Exec. VP for Health & Public Policy, American College of Physicians

Chief Exec. VP (specialty medical society)

Deputy Exec. VP (state medical society)

Deputy Medical Director, American Psychiatric Association (4)

Director, Medical Services Division, NY State Medical Society

Director, The New York Academy of Medicine

Director, Office of International Medicine, American College of Surgeons

Director, Scientific Publications Division, NY State Medical Society

Executive Director

American Association of Immunology

American Fertility Association

American Osteopathic Association

American Public Health Association

Educational Commission for Foreign Medical Graduates

Federation of State Medical Boards, Inc.

International Council of Societies of Pathology

Private Doctors of America

Society for Epidemiology & Voluntary Assistance

World Society for Stereotactic & Functional Neurosurgery

Executive Officer

American Health Care Association

American Society for Pharmacology & Experimental Therapeutics, Inc.

International Association of Coroners & Medical Examiners

Executive Secretary/Executive VP

American Society of Internal Medicine

Council of Medical Specialty Societies

Federation of State Medical Boards of the United States

International College of Surgeons

Undersea Medical Society

President, Association of Academic Health Centers

President, Greater NY Hospital Association

Project Manager, International Health, American Public Health Association

Scientific Program Coordinator, American Public Health Association

VP, Division of Science & Technology, Pharmaceutical Manufacturers Association

VP for Medical & Scientific Affairs, Proprietary Association

12. Research (Nongovernment)

Associate Director for Clinical Research, Institute for Cancer Research

Director

Arthur V. Davis Center for Behavior Neurobiology, Salk Institute

Graduate Pain Research Foundation

New American Research Institute (Chicago)

Palm Beach Institute for Medical Research

Quincy Research Center (Kansas City)

Research & Development, InterQual (Chicago)

Res. Institute of Lab. Medicine, Pacific Med. Center, Institute of Med. Sciences

Director & Resident Fellow, Salk Institute

Director for Education, Mayo Foundation

Director of Research, Mayo Foundation

Director of Research, San Diego Zoo

Executive Director, Philadelphia Association for Clinical Trials

Investigator, International Fertility (Research Triangle Park, NC)

Medical Associate, International Program, The Population Council (NYC)

Medical Consultant, The Institute for Aerobics Research (Dallas)

Medical Manager, Cardiovascular Research

President

Beneficial Plant Research Associate

Biometric Testing (Englewood Cliffs, NJ)

President

Drug Abuse Council

International Institute of Stress, University of Montreal

Memorial Sloan-Kettering Cancer Ctr (NYC)

Rockburn Institute (Elkridge, MD)

Sidney Farber Cancer Institute

Research Associate, Harvard Botanical Museum

Research Associate, MIT Arteriosclerosis Center

Research Associate, Medical Research Center, Brookhaven National Laboratory

Research Fellow, Infectious Disease, Dept. of Medicine (New England Medical Center Hospital)

Research Scientist, Health Service Research Center (Univ. of Michigan)

Senior Fellow, The Population Council (NYC) (12)

Senior Health Services Researcher (The RAND Corp.)

Team Member, Health & Nutrition Examination Survey (private consulting firm)

VP & CEO, Chicago Technology Park

American League (baseball)

Center for Corporate Health Promotion (Reston, VA)

Commission on Prof. & Hospital Activities

Employment Agency

Institute for Generic Drugs

Management Sciences for Health (Boston)

Producer & Director of Films for Television

Secretary-Treasurer, International Health Society (Englewood, CO)

Senior Professional Associate, Institute of Medicine, National Research Council

Senior Research Associate, Health Policy Program, Urban Institute

13. Miscellaneous

Anthropologist

Author

Chairman, Cable Health Network (television)

Conductor, Symphony Orchestra

Director, Drug Standards Division, United States Pharmacopeia

Director, Occupational Health, United Mine Workers of America

Dir., Public Citizen, Inc. (Washington, DC)

Exec. Dir., Institute for Health Planning

Exec. Direction, Nutrition Foundation

Homesteader

Investment Counselor

Medical Consultant, The

President
  American Health Care Institute

14. Part-time Activities

(Compensation received but doctor still spends 80% or more time as a clinician or nonclinician)

Athletic Team Physician

Author

Chairman, National Digestive Diseases Advisory Board, U.S. Dept. of HHS

Chairman, Princeton Institute for Health Policy

Clinical Professor of Medicine or Surgery

Commissioner, Dept. of Health Services (county)

Chief Exec. Officer (specialty medical society)

Concert Pianist

Consultant, U.S. Secret Police

Consultant, Fire or Police Dept.; Worker's Compensation Commission

Coroner/Medical Examiner (county or city)

Designer (contemporary women's fashions)

Editor (national/state/county medical journal)

Editorial Consultant/Editorial Review Board

Expert Witness

Foreign Language Interpreter

Magician

Mayor (Coos Bay, OR)

Medical Director, World Boxing Hall of Fame

Medical Illustrator

Member, Board of Directors (manufacturing firms)

Member, State Legislature

Photographer

President, Flying Physicians Association

President, National Council on Marijuana

President, National Society to Prevent Blindness

School Physician

Index